REWARD

Elementary

Practice Book

Diana Pye
Simon Greenall

MACMILLAN
HEINEMANN
English Language Teaching

1 What's your name?

VOCABULARY

1 Match the towns with the countries.

Rome	Australia
Rio de Janeiro	Russia
Washington	Turkey
Moscow	Italy
Sydney	the United States of America
Istanbul	Brazil

2 Find 17 countries in the puzzle. They go (→) and (↓).

S	P	A	I	N	I	N	D	I	A
P	A	R	G	E	N	T	I	N	A
E	G	F	T	U	R	K	E	Y	T
R	R	R	C	I	U	O	B	Y	H
U	E	A	H	T	S	R	R	M	A
J	E	N	I	A	S	E	I	E	I
A	C	C	N	L	I	A	T	X	L
P	E	E	A	Y	A	I	A	I	A
A	C	A	N	A	D	A	I	C	N
N	B	R	A	Z	I	L	N	O	D

3 Match these towns with six countries in the puzzle. Write sentences.

Madrid Seoul Buenos Aires Paris Tokyo Athens Lima

Madrid is in Spain.

1 ______
2 ______
3 ______
4 ______
5 ______
6 ______

FUNCTIONS

1 Put the words in order and write sentences.

1 what your is name?
______
2 from where you are?
______
3 is my Charlie name.
______
4 from am I Canada.
______
5 name Maria your is?
______

2 Match the correct answers with the three questions in activity 1.

a No, my name's Anna.
b My name's Juan.
c I'm from the United States.

3 Write your answers to the questions in activity 1.

1 ______
2 ______
3 ______

4 Underline the verbs. Circle the subject pronouns.

is what your the am Mary from name you where I are hello my Brazil be yes

5 Write five sentences with the words in activity 4.

1 ______
2 ______
3 ______
4 ______
5 ______

SOUNDS

1 Listen and tick (✓) the countries you hear.

China Japan Turkey Italy Brazil Mexico
Hungary Spain Britain Germany Russia Korea
Thailand Canada Ukraine Poland Morocco

2 Put the countries with a tick in the right columns.

o O	O o	O o o	o O o
	China		

Listen again and check.

LISTENING

1 Listen to four conversations. Match the conversations with the pictures.

A ☐

2 Listen again and complete the conversations with these countries.

1 the United States of America
2 Italy
3 Australia
4 Spain
5 Canada
6 Britain
7 Sweden
8 France

Conversation 1

A Hello, I'm Juan.
B Hello, Juan. My name's Anna. I'm from __________ . Where are you from, Juan?
A I'm from __________ .

Conversation 2

C Hello, my name's Thomas, Peter Thomas.
D Hello, Mr Thomas. I'm Marco Placidi. I'm from __________ . Where are you from?
C I'm from ____________________ .

Conversation 3

E Hello, I'm Ingrid. What's your name?
F Hello, Ingrid. My name's Sally. Where are you from?
E I'm from __________. And you, Sally? Where are you from?
F I'm from __________ .

Conversation 4

G Hello, my name's Janet Smith.
H Hello, Mrs Smith. I'm Marilyn Kelly.
G Where are you from, Mrs Kelly?
H I'm from __________ .

B ☐

C ☐ D ☐

2 This is Bruno and Maria

VOCABULARY

1 Underline the jobs.

teacher student town name waiter where receptionist country tourist doctor chef nationality actor artist police officer nurse their journalist

2 What are their jobs? Look at the pictures and write sentences.

1 He's a ______________.
2 She's an ______________.
3 He ______________.
4 She ______________.
5 He ______________.
6 They ______________.

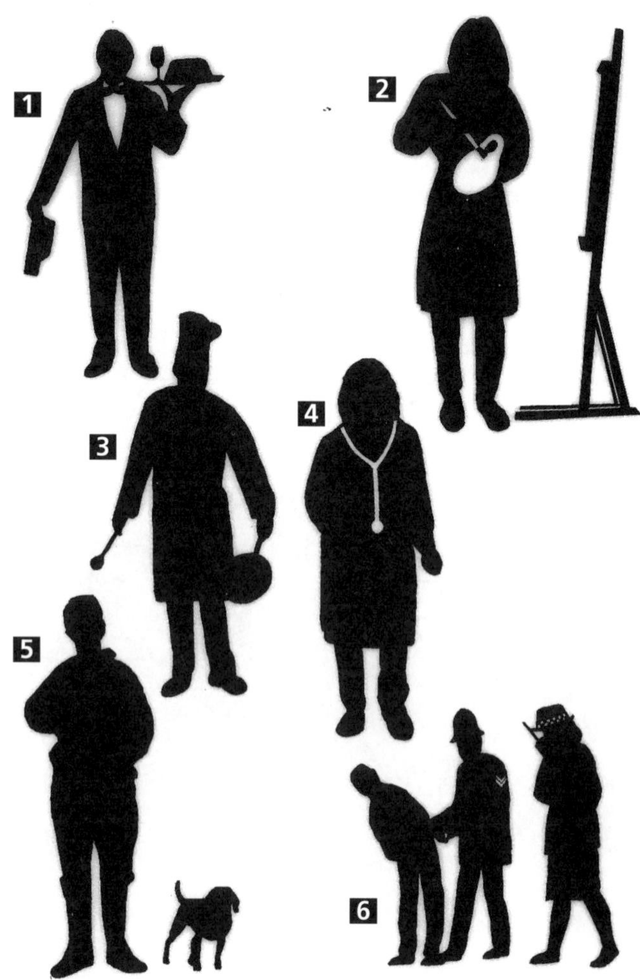

3 Circle the odd-word-out.

1 he she her you they
2 Brazil Croatia Moscow Greece China
3 my we our their his
4 Prague Seoul Ankara Brazil Madrid
5 friend teacher journalist technician accountant
6 I'm your he's she's you're

4 Write sentences with the odd-word-out.

1 *Her name is Helena.*
2 ______________
3 ______________
4 ______________
5 ______________
6 ______________

GRAMMAR

1 Underline the correct form.

1 *They're/Their* German.
2 *You're/Your* from Barcelona.
3 *They're/Their* friend is a doctor.
4 What nationality is *you're/your* friend?
5 *They're/Their* parents are from Poland.

2 Write *his* or *he's*.

1 __________ from Mexico.
2 __________ name is Karl.
3 __________ Italian.
4 What's __________ name?
5 __________ a student.

3 Replace the names with a subject pronoun.

Artur is from Poland.
He's from Poland.

1 Maria is a secretary.
____

2 John and Chrissie are from Australia.
____

3 Kevin is an actor.

____

4 Paul and Karl are doctors.

____

5 My brother and I are farmers.

____

4 Write the full form of the verbs.

What's your name?
What is your name?

1 He's a teacher.

____

2 They're from Thailand.

____

3 I'm Spanish.

____

4 We're students.

____

5 They're actors.

____

6 She's a doctor.

____

READING

1 Read the descriptions. What are their jobs? Write sentences.

1 *Maria is a receptionist.*
2 Jim ____________________
3 Isabella ____________________
4 Yannick ____________________
5 Emma ____________________

A My name is Maria. I'm from Milan and I'm Italian. I'm a receptionist in a hotel in London. My boyfriend is British. His name is Jim and he's a jazz musician.

B My name is Yannick. I'm from France. I'm a journalist for an international magazine. My wife's name is Isabella and she's from Barcelona. She's an economist.

C I'm Emma Simpson. I'm a nurse in Edinburgh but I'm from London. My parents are teachers at the university here.

2 Correct these sentences.

1 Yannick is from Spain.

____

2 Maria is from London.

____

3 Emma is a student.

____

4 Jim is an actor.

____

5 Emma's parents are doctors.

____

3 Rewrite description B in the third person.

His name is Yannick.

____

____

____

____

____

LISTENING

1 Listen to the conversation. Underline things that are different.

A Hi there. My name's Jan. I'm from Britain. I'm a computer technician here at the university.
B Hello, Jan. My name's Lee. I'm from Vancouver in Canada. I'm a student.
A This is my friend, Sara. She's from France. She's a teacher.
B Hello, Sara.
C Hello, Lee.

2 Complete the conversation with *his, he's* or *he*.

A Hello, Peter. What's your friend's name?
B __________ name's Silvio.
A Where's __________ from?
B __________ from Italy.
A What's __________ job?
B __________ an accountant.

Listen and check.

3 Questions, questions

VOCABULARY

1 Circle the nouns and underline the adjectives.

married student his children are her
Japan there from doctor single surname
phone number he brother is actor not am
friend where good-looking address
first name what job boyfriend

2 Write sentences with five of the nouns in activity 1.

1 ______
2 ______
3 ______
4 ______
5 ______

GRAMMAR

1 Match the questions and the answers.

1	How old is he?	a	Rosslare in Ireland.
2	What's her job?	b	Fine, thanks.
3	Who's this?	c	He's thirteen years old.
4	Where are you from?	d	She's a nurse.
5	What's your telephone number?	e	Ann Smith.
6	How are you?	f	01478 859 321.

2 Complete with a question word: *What, Where, How* or *Who*.

1 ______ are you from?
2 ______ old are you?
3 ______ is your address?
4 ______ is your favourite actor?
5 ______ is your home?
6 ______ is your telephone number?

3 Answer the questions in activity 2.

1 ______
2 ______
3 ______
4 ______
5 ______
6 ______

4 Write questions for these answers.

1 ______
No, she's single.
2 ______
No, I'm married.
3 ______
Yes, his children are medical students.
4 ______
No, he isn't, he's from London.
5 ______
No, I'm a journalist.
6 ______
Yes, she's a French teacher at the university.

5 Disagree with the sentences.

He's from London. (Oxford)
No, he isn't. He's from Oxford.

1 She's from Hungary. (Romania)
______
2 He's a doctor. (nurse)
______
3 They're Spanish. (Argentinian)
______
4 She's eighteen. (seventeen)
______
5 He's single. (married)
______

SOUNDS

Listen to the questions in *Grammar* activity 2. Notice the intonation.

Listen again and repeat.

LISTENING

1 Listen to a conversation. What is the situation?

at the doctor's ☐ at the police station ☐

at a job interview ☐ at a business meeting ☐

2 Listen again. Write down four questions the interviewer asks.

1 ______

2 ______

3 ______

4 ______

3 Correct these sentences.

Maria is a hotel manager.

No, she isn't. She's a receptionist.

1 Maria is married.

______

2 Maria is twenty years old.

______

3 Maria is British.

______

WRITING

1 Match the people in the pictures with the information in their passports. There is one extra picture.

2 Write descriptions of two of the people.

______

______

______

______

______

______

______

______

SURNAME	Haines
FIRST NAME	Michael
ADDRESS	3, End Street, Cardiff
DATE OF BIRTH	12 November 1942
PLACE OF BIRTH	Bristol
SEX	M
CHILDREN	2
OCCUPATION	Airline pilot

SURNAME	Singh
FIRST NAME	Janvi
ADDRESS	24, Thames Road, Reading
DATE OF BIRTH	3 May 1967
PLACE OF BIRTH	London
SEX	F
CHILDREN	None
OCCUPATION	Doctor

SURNAME	Downs
FIRST NAME	May
ADDRESS	Grove Cottage, Hay
DATE OF BIRTH	14 January 1927
PLACE OF BIRTH	Bristol
SEX	F
CHILDREN	5
OCCUPATION	Retired

How many students are there?

VOCABULARY

1 Circle the odd-word-out.

1 kind lovely room friendly good
2 eight twelve chair fifty nine
3 interesting book room school computer
4 where how who what that

2 Write sentences with the odd-words-out in activity 1.

1 __________
2 __________
3 __________
4 __________

3 Complete the sentences with one of these adjectives.

good beautiful comfortable kind interesting

1 He's a __________ man.
2 She's a __________ teacher.
3 It's an __________ lesson.
4 It's a __________ chair.
5 It's a __________ city.

GRAMMAR AND SOUNDS

1 Listen and write the numbers.

____
____
____

Now say all the numbers aloud.

2 Write the plurals of these words.

classroom __________
teacher __________
address __________
number __________
college __________
class __________
chair __________

Listen and check. Say the words aloud.

3 Write sentences with *there is* or *there are*.

thirty desks in the room
There are thirty desks in the room.

1 a book and a pen on the table
____
2 three students in the classroom
____
3 a computer on the table
____
4 two good schools in the town
____
5 a cassette player in the room
____

4 Listen and put the words with *th* in two groups.

thirteen this their three with there thanks the they think

/θ/ *thirteen* __________
____
/ð/ *this* __________
____

READING

1 Read the description of a school. What type of school is it?

____

2 Underline the adjectives in the passage.

3 Answer the questions.

1 Is it a big school?

____

2 Is it for adults or children?

____

3 How old are the writer's children?

____

4 Where is the school?

____

5 Is it a very modern school?

____

My two children are at a new bilingual school in the town centre. There are English and Italian children in each class. The lessons are in English and Italian. The school is in an old building but the classrooms are very modern. It's not a very big school. There are fifty pupils from six to ten years of age. There are four classes. The teachers are very friendly and their English is very good. My children are six and nine years old. The classrooms are big and comfortable. There's a big library with a television and video. There's also a special room with twelve computers. There's a small garden for the children. It's a very good school but it's also a very expensive school.

WRITING

1 Look at the passage in *Reading* again. Write a similar description of your school.

____

____

____

____

____

____

____

____

2 Read these sentences. Put a tick (✓) by the sentences which describe your classroom.

1 It's big and comfortable. ☐

2 It isn't very modern. ☐

3 There are tables and chairs. ☐

4 There isn't a computer. ☐

5 There is a tape recorder. ☐

6 There is a blackboard. ☐

7 There is a big window. ☐

8 There is a television and video. ☐

3 Write a description of your classroom.

____

____

____

____

____

____

____

____

5 *Where's my pen?*

VOCABULARY

1 Put the words into the correct categories.

accountant calculator camera city computer country diary doctor farmer library mobile phone notebook pen pencil personal stereo radio school vet

Electronic products: ____________________
Office things: ____________________
Jobs: ____________________
Places: ____________________

2 Label the objects.

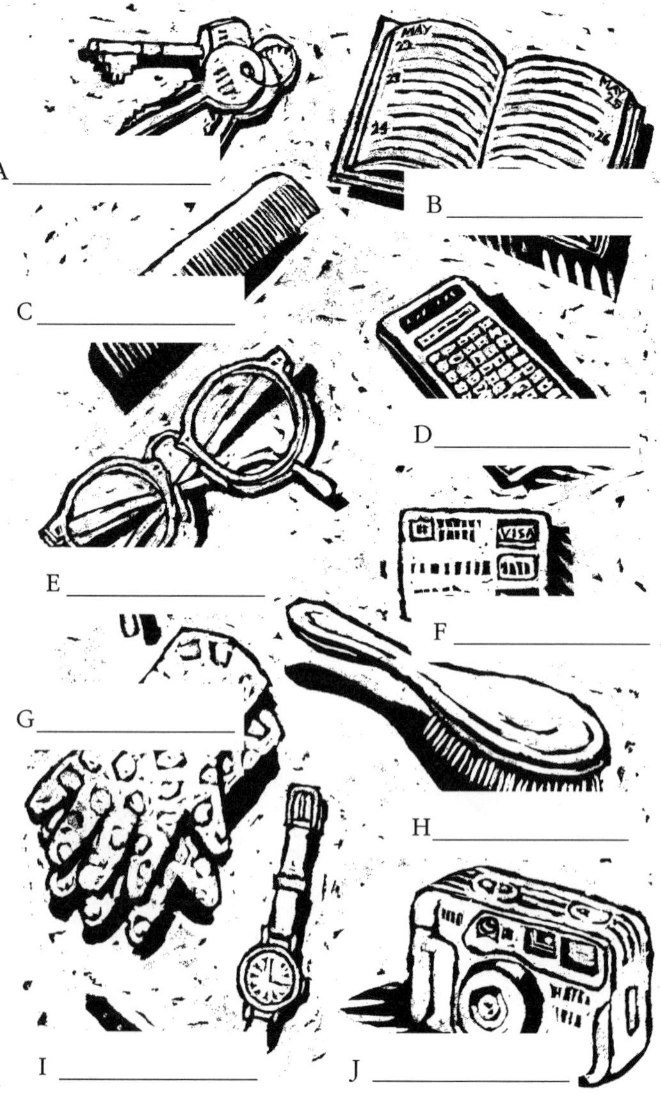

A ______________
B ______________
C ______________
D ______________
E ______________
F ______________
G ______________
H ______________
I ______________
J ______________

3 Write the correct preposition.

on under in near

A B C D

4 Complete the questions.

Where What How

1 __________ do you spell *wallet*?
2 __________ is this in English?
3 __________ colour is your bag?
4 __________ is your pen?

GRAMMAR

1 Rewrite the sentences without the contractions.

We're from London.
We are from London.

1 He's got a new video.
____
2 They've got a television and a video.
____
3 She's a secretary at the bank.
____
4 I've got a hat and gloves in my bag.
____
5 She's got a mobile phone in her bag.
____
6 He's twenty-five years old today.
____

2 What have you got? Write five sentences.

I've got three keys.
1 ____________________
2 ____________________
3 ____________________
4 ____________________
5 ____________________

3 Where are they? Write sentences.

your car
It's in the car park.

1 your diary

2 your telephone

3 your Student's Book

4 your bag

5 your coat

SOUNDS

1 Listen and write the words.

1	_ A _ _ E T	4	_ _ _ E R _
2	_ _ L O U _	5	W _ _ _ H
3	_ _ M B	6	_ I _ R _

2 Listen and notice the pronunciation of the underlined letters.

1 It's the black key.
2 He's got a pink car.
3 I've got a black coat.
4 He's got a red telephone.
5 There's a red diary on the table.

Listen again and repeat.

3 Listen and repeat.

radio stereo video phone mobile coat comb

LISTENING

Listen to the conversation and complete it.

A Where are my ________?
B What ________ are they?
A ________ and ________. They're not in my ________.
B Well, they're not ________ the table. Are they ________ your book?
A Oh, yes. Here they are. Thanks.

WRITING

Describe the room.

6 Families

VOCABULARY

1 Complete the chart.

Male	Female
man	______
______	girl
father	______
______	sister
______	niece
son	______
husband	______
______	aunt
grandfather	______
cousin	______

2 Complete the sentences with words from the chart in activity 1.

1 My mother's sister is my ______.
2 My brother's daughter is my ______.
3 My father's mother is my ______.
4 My daughter's brother is my ______.
5 My mother and father's son is my ______.
6 My aunt's son is my ______.

3 Write the plurals.

man ______
woman ______
child ______
family ______
person ______
wife ______
country ______

READING AND GRAMMAR

1 Look at the pictures and write sentences about the families.

Family A:
There are four people in the family.
______
______

Family B:
______
______

2 Look at the passage. Two texts are mixed up. The texts are descriptions of the two families in the pictures. Read the passage and underline the description of family A.

Jenny is thirty-two years old and has got a job in a post office in a small village. Peter is thirty-nine years old and he is an architect in London. He is married to Elizabeth and they've got four children: three sons and a daughter. She's divorced and has got an eight-year-old daughter, Cilla, and a three-year-old son, Jamie. She's got a small house with a big garden in the village. They live in a big house near London. She's got a lot of friends in the village. Elizabeth looks after the children and has a part-time job in a school near her home. Jenny's mother, Kate, lives in the same village. Peter's parents, Fiona and Michael, live in the country and come to stay with the family in the holidays. They have a comfortable life and they are a happy family. She helps Jenny with the children when she's at work.

A

B

3 Correct these false statements.

1 Jenny's husband is Peter.

____

2 Elizabeth is an architect.

____

3 Peter has got two children.

____

4 Jenny has got a part-time job in a school.

____

5 Jenny has got a house near London.

____

4 Who are they?

Kate *is Jenny's mother.*

1 Elizabeth

____

2 Fiona and Michael

____

3 Cilla

____

4 Jamie

____

5 Look at the family tree. Write sentences describing relationships.

Timothy Helen

Mary Josh Kevin Christine Sally Greg Henry

Jane Harry John Philippa

Helen is John's grandmother.
Jane has got one brother and two cousins.

____

LISTENING

1 Look at the family tree in *Grammar* activity 5. Listen to two of the people talking about their family. Who are the speakers?

Speaker 1: _______________

Speaker 2: _______________

2 Listen again. Complete the information about members of the family.

1 Sally has got an interesting job; she's a _______________.

2 Philippa is _______________ years old.

3 Greg is not British, he's _______________.

4 Greg has got a job with a _______________ company.

5 Henry is not _______________.

WRITING

Draw your own family tree and write sentences describing relationships in your family.

____

7 What's the time?

VOCABULARY

1 What time is it?

3.30 pm: *It's half past three in the afternoon.*

1 4.20 pm: ______

2 10.45 am: ______

3 9.00 pm: ______

4 11.30 am: ______

5 6.15 am: ______

2 Put these activities in order. Number the boxes.

have lunch ☐

go to bed ☐

finish work ☐

have breakfast ☐

start work ☐

have dinner ☐

get up ☐

3 Say when you do the things in activity 2.

1 *I get up at seven o'clock.*

2 ______

3 ______

4 ______

5 ______

6 ______

7 ______

READING

1 Read the passage. Underline the prepositions of time.

2 Write down things that are different in your country.

We don't start work at nine o'clock, we start work at half past eight.

______

______

______

______

______

The French day

Most people start work at nine in the morning and finish work at five in the evening. But teachers and schoolchildren start work at eight and finish at five. It's a very long day in a French school. Most people don't work at weekends. Some children go to school on Saturday mornings, but they don't go to school on Wednesday afternoons. The French have a small breakfast before they go to work. They have two hours at lunchtime and they usually have a big lunch. Many people go to restaurants at midday. In the evening they have another big meal at about eight o'clock.

GRAMMAR

1 Write the correct preposition: *in, at* or *on*.

1 _____ the morning
2 _____ midday
3 _____ the weekend
4 _____ night
5 _____ the evening
6 _____ Sunday
7 _____ 7 o'clock
8 _____ Monday

2 Write sentences for the times in activity 1.

1 *I go to work at nine in the morning.*
2 ______
3 ______
4 ______
5 ______
6 ______
7 ______
8 ______

3 Answer the questions about people in your country.

1 What time do children go to school?
______
2 What time do teachers start and finish work?
______
3 When do most people finish work?
______
4 What time do people have their lunch?
______

SOUNDS

1 Listen to the questions. Underline the stressed words.

1 Do you work at the weekend?
2 Do people work on Sunday mornings?
3 Do they have lunch at home?
4 Do we finish work at five today?
5 Do you have a siesta in the afternoon?

Listen again and repeat.

2 Circle the word with a different vowel sound.

1 no don't home work most
2 son clock some much M<u>o</u>nday
3 night time five write girl
4 t<u>ea</u>cher three br<u>ea</u>kfast people week

Listen and check. Say the words aloud.

3 Listen and write down the times.

1 *3.30*
2 ______
3 ______
4 ______
5 ______
6 ______
7 ______
8 ______
9 ______
10 ______

WRITING

Look back at the passage in *Reading*. Write a passage describing what you do when you are on holiday. What is different from your workday routine?

When I'm on holiday I get up at ten o'clock.

______

8 Home

VOCABULARY

1 Write down as many words as you can in these categories.

Furniture: __________

Electrical equipment: __________

2 Write down five very useful things in your home. Where are these things?

telephone: There is a telephone on the table in the hall next to the door.

1 __________
2 __________
3 __________
4 __________
5 __________

3 Write down the names of the rooms in your home.

____
____

4 Say what you do in these rooms.

____
____
____
____
____

GRAMMAR

1 Complete the sentences with *is* or *are*.

1 There __________ four bedrooms.
2 There __________ a sitting room with a sofa.
3 There __________ some chairs next to the table.
4 There __________ (not) any books.
5 __________ there any curtains in the bedroom?
6 There __________ (not) a video.
7 __________ there a dishwasher?
8 There __________ a car in the garage.

2 Complete the sentences with *some* or *any*.

1 There aren't __________ armchairs in the bedrooms.
2 There are __________ books on the shelf.
3 There are __________ shutters in the room upstairs.
4 Are there __________ plants in the sitting room?
5 He hasn't got __________ curtains in his room.
6 They have __________ videos in the cupboard.

LISTENING

1 Listen to three people describing their favourite rooms. What rooms do the people describe?

Speaker 1: __________
Speaker 2: __________
Speaker 3: __________

2 Listen again and complete the sentences.

Room 1

1 My favourite room is a small __________.
2 It is __________ next to the __________.
3 There are __________ on two walls of the room.
4 In front of the __________ is a desk with my __________.
5 There is a big __________ on the wall next to a very old __________.

Room 2

1 My favourite room is a big __________ at the back of the house.
2 There is a __________ with a view of the __________.
3 There is a comfortable __________ in front of the __________.
4 There are some pretty green __________ and an old __________.
5 The __________ and __________ are on a cupboard near the fire.

Room 3

1 I like my __________ best of all.
2 It's __________ at the front of the house.
3 There's a __________ and a small table with a __________.
4 There's a __________ next to the door.
5 There are some ______________________ on the table near the window.

SOUNDS

1 **How do you pronounce the letter *a* in these words? Listen and put the words into two groups.**

armchair bath bookcase carpet game garden large plane plant radio table washbasin

/ɑː/ armchair

/eɪ/ bookcase

2 **Listen and repeat these words with *sh* and *ch*.**

/ʃ/ shutters shower dishwasher washbasin possession shirt

/tʃ/ kitchen chair furniture watch coach check lunch

WRITING AND READING

1 **Where are these things in your house? Write sentences.**

bathroom radio bed telephone bookcase plants mirror cooker garage

The bathroom is upstairs next to my bedroom.

2 **Mr and Mrs Edmunds want to do a house exchange with a family in another country. Read the description of their home which is in a house exchange brochure.**

Where do Mr and Mrs Edmunds want to go for their holiday?

3 **Are these sentences true or false?**

1 Mr and Mrs Edmunds have got two children.
2 They've got a house near Cambridge.
3 There is a small garden at the front of the house.
4 Their holiday is in August.
5 There isn't a garage.

Mr and Mrs G Edmunds
The Old Mill
Burwell
Cambridgeshire
Telephone: 01223 639 487

Holiday dates: 1st July to 21st July
Exchange with a house with a garden suitable for a family of five people (two adults and three small children) in Italy.

Our house is in a pretty village near Cambridge. It is in a beautiful place next to a river. It is very quiet and safe for children. The house is suitable for five people. It is quite big and there is a garden at the back. There are three bedrooms, a bathroom and a toilet upstairs. Downstairs there is a sitting room with a fire, two armchairs and a sofa. There are carpets in all the bedrooms and in the sitting room. The kitchen is at the back of the house and there is a door to the garden.

There is a dishwasher, a cooker, a washing machine and a fridge in the kitchen. There is a downstairs toilet and shower. Next to the kitchen is a small dining room. There are two telephones, a television and stereo equipment in the house. There is no garage.

4 **Write a similar description of your home for the house exchange.**

9 How do you relax?

VOCABULARY

1 Find 21 verbs in the puzzle. They go (→) and (↓).

R	E	L	A	X	L	I	V	E
E	W	A	T	C	H	G	E	T
A	A	H	D	R	I	N	K	F
D	S	A	M	A	K	E	S	I
L	H	V	P	L	A	Y	T	N
E	W	E	C	L	D	O	A	I
A	O	S	O	I	G	O	R	S
R	R	E	M	K	E	A	T	H
N	K	E	E	E	S	I	N	G

2 Complete the sentences with verbs from the puzzle.

1 I __________ a sauna on Wednesday evenings.
2 I __________ sport on television on Saturday afternoons.
3 I __________ the Sunday lunch for the family.
4 I __________ a sandwich and __________ mineral water for lunch.
5 I __________ the guitar in a rock band with friends.
6 I __________ Spanish at evening classes.

GRAMMAR

1 Write the sentences in *Vocabulary* activity 2 in the third person singular.

1 ____________________
2 ____________________
3 ____________________
4 ____________________
5 ____________________
6 ____________________

2 Complete with a suitable question word.

1 __________ do you live?
2 __________ do you relax?
3 __________ do you live with?
4 __________ do you do on Sundays?
5 __________ do you start work?

3 Answer the questions in activity 2.

1 ____________________
2 ____________________
3 ____________________
4 ____________________
5 ____________________

4 What do you do ...

1 at lunchtime?
____
2 on Sunday mornings?
____
3 on weekday evenings?
____
4 on Saturday evenings?
____

READING

1 Read the passage. Is the writer a man or a woman?

____

2 Find four things the writer does alone. Write sentences in the third person singular.

____
____
____
____

3 Write down three things his wife does alone. Write sentences in the third person singular.

____

____

____

4 Underline the things they do together.

On weekdays my wife comes home at 6.30 and I come home at 7. We have a drink and then I make dinner. We sit and have dinner in front of the television. On Tuesday evenings we go to the cinema with friends and then we have a drink in a bar in town. On Wednesday evenings my wife goes to language classes and then she goes to a friend's house for dinner. I watch the sport on television when she isn't there.

At the weekend we get up at midday. On Saturday afternoon we go to the supermarket for things for the week. After that I go running or I read. In the evening we go to a restaurant with friends or to a nightclub. On Sundays we go to my wife's parents' house in the country. In the evening I watch television and my wife works on her computer. ●

LISTENING

1 Listen to two women. Tick (✓) the things they do alone.

	Woman 1	Woman 2
reads the newspaper		
has a cup of tea		
makes dinner		
goes to a friend's house		
has a language class		
has dinner with a friend		
goes running		
goes to a jazz club		
works on her computer		

2 Listen again and decide which woman is the wife of the man in the passage in *Reading*.

SOUNDS

1 Listen and circle the word in each line with a different-sounding ending.

1 does goes gets plays
2 eats has likes drinks
3 watches makes finishes relaxes
4 sees reads lives speaks

Listen and check. Say the words aloud.

2 Listen to the sentences. The underlined sounds are said together.

1 We get up at eight o'clock.
2 I get a video.
3 I watch it at night.
4 He learns a language.
5 She gets up for work.
6 He lives at home.

Listen again and repeat.

WRITING

What do you do with your friends in your free time? Write four or five sentences.

____

____

____

____

____

____

____

____

10 Do you like jazz?

SOUNDS

1 How many syllables are there in these words? Put them in the correct list. Underline the stressed syllables.

football computer magazine unemployed afternoon country singer cinema classical tennis programme skating

Two syllables ______________________

____

Three syllables ______________________

____

Listen and repeat.

2 Listen and repeat these questions.

1 Who's your favourite writer?
2 What type of films do you like?
3 What about you?
4 What Chinese restaurant do you go to?
5 Where do you go dancing?

VOCABULARY

1 Write down nouns you associate with these verbs.

play ______________________
watch ______________________
listen to ______________________

2 Write sentences with words from activity 1.

____
____
____
____
____

READING

Put the questions into the conversation.

A (1)
B I love tennis. I play most afternoons. (2)
A I don't like playing it very much. I only watch it on TV.
B (3)
A I like Pete Sampras.
B Yeah, he's great! (4)
A I like swimming, running and skiing in the winter. (5)
B No, I don't. But I like skating.

a What other sports do you like?
b Do you go skiing?
c What's your favourite sport?
d What about you?
e Who's your favourite player?

GRAMMAR

1 Complete the chart with the object pronouns.

Subject	Object
I	*me*
you	
he	
she	
it	
we	
they	

2 Replace the underlined word(s) by a pronoun object from the chart.

I like Italian films very much.
I like them very much.

1 I love modern jazz.

2 I don't like westerns.

3 I don't like classical music.

4 I like Emma Thompson very much.

5 I hate computer games.

6 I really like my uncle.

3 Put the words in order and write sentences.

1 you music do like classical?

2 of do type music like you what?

3 skiing at like not I do all.

4 like to cinema do the going you?

5 it not much like do I very.

4 Say what you like or don't like *doing*. Use these verbs.

play watch listen to eat drink go

jazz *I like listening to jazz.*

1 Chinese food

2 television

3 the cinema

4 computer games

5 tea

LISTENING

1 Listen to two conversations. What are the situations?

a in an art gallery
b at a night club
c at a concert
d at a restaurant

2 Listen again and tick (✓) what they like.

	Man	Woman
modern art	☐	☐
classical art	☐	☐
reggae	☐	☐
classical music	☐	☐
dancing	☐	☐

WRITING

1 Write about three things you like very much and three things you don't like at all.

2 Write a conversation for one of the other situations in *Listening* activity 1.

11 A day in my life

VOCABULARY AND GRAMMAR

1 Underline the adjectives.

late usually punctual often early sometimes on time never always

2 Complete these sentences with words from activity 1. Make the sentences true for you.

1 I __________ get to work on time.
2 I usually get up __________.
3 I __________ have a big breakfast.
4 I __________ arrive a few minutes late for my English class.
5 I always arrive __________ for an important meeting.
6 I __________ do the housework at weekends.

3 Write down five things you do regularly.

get up
____
____
____

4 Write five sentences with the things in activity 3. Say what time and how often you do them.

I usually get up at seven o'clock in the morning.
1 __________
2 __________
3 __________
4 __________
5 __________

SOUNDS

1 Say these times.

6 o'clock 3.15 4.30 2.10 6.45 9.50 10.05 7.20

Listen and check.

2 Do the speakers sound happy or unhappy?

1 I always arrive on time.
2 I never go out to dinner.
3 He always gets here late.
4 She never cooks the lunch.
5 They never see their parents.
6 I always do the washing up.

Listen again and underline the stressed words.

3 Continue the sentences in activity 2 with a few words or a sentence.

1 *I always arrive on time for an important meeting.*
or *I always arrive on time. I don't like arriving late.*
2 __________
3 __________
4 __________
5 __________
6 __________

LISTENING

1 Write down words you associate with these jobs.

taxi *driver drive*
teacher __________
chef __________
musician __________

2 Who do you think works these hours? Match them with the jobs in activity 1. Then write a sentence for each job.

He/she works from seven o'clock in the morning to two o'clock in the afternoon.

a from 9.00 am to 4.30 pm
____
____

b from 8.15 pm to 2.00 am

____

____

c from 10 am to 2.15 pm and from 6.45 pm to 11.00 pm

____

____

d from 8.00 pm to 6.15 am

____

____

3 Listen to two people talking about their working day. Match the speakers with the jobs in activity 1.

Speaker 1 ______________

Speaker 2 ______________

4 Listen again and match the sentences with the speakers. There are two extra sentences.

1 On the nights we play I have a snack at home at 7 o'clock.
2 I leave the house at 9.40.
3 I prepare my lessons and correct pupils' work in the evenings.
4 We usually start playing at 9.00 but I always get to the club at 8.15 to get things ready.
5 My wife works in the mornings and she is usually at the house when I get home.
6 We usually play for an hour and a half, then we have a break.
7 We always have a snack and a drink.
8 I don't go to work on Sundays and Mondays.
9 I get the bus at 8.30 and get to school at 9.50.
10 I get up at 8.00 most mornings and have a shower and a big breakfast with my wife.

5 What job in activity 1 do you think the two extra sentences describe?

Write three more sentences for this job.

____

____

____

____

____

6 Complete the sentences with verbs from the list.

get go leave get up have work read

I (1) _________ at 8 o'clock most mornings and (2) _________ a shower and a big breakfast with my wife. My wife (3) _________ for work at 8.45 and I relax and (4) _________ the newspaper for half an hour. I (5) _________ the house at 9.40 and walk to work. I (6) _________ lunch at the restaurant at 2 o'clock and then I walk home. My wife (7) _________ in the mornings and she is usually at the house when I (8) _________ home. In the afternoon I relax at home or go out to the park with my wife. At six o'clock I (9) _________ back to work and I (10) _________ home at 11 o'clock. I don't go to work on Sundays and Mondays.

WRITING

1 Write a summary of the musician's working day. Use the third person singular.

____

____

____

____

____

____

____

____

____

____

2 Write sentences about these situations. Use the words in *Vocabulary and Grammar* activity 1.

dentist work dinner party theatre English class

I always arrive early for an appointment with the dentist.

____

____

____

____

____

12 How do you get to work?

VOCABULARY

Look at the pictures and write words and phrases you can use to describe these means of transport.

A ______________________________

____

B ______________________________

____

C ______________________________

____

READING

1 Read the passage and match the description with one of the pictures.

2 Underline the disadvantages of this means of transport.

3 What is the only advantage mentioned in the description?

4 Look at your list of words in *Vocabulary*. How many words are the same as in the passage?

In Pakistan most people travel by bus to get from one town to another. In the less populated parts of the country many journeys take a day and there is a bus only once or twice a week. It is a dangerous means of transport and the buses sometimes break down. The roads are often in bad condition and the journeys are very slow and uncomfortable. It is a good idea to take food and drink because there are not always restaurants or shops on the route. The buses are usually very crowded with whole families travelling together. Many people sit on the roof where it is very hot in the summer and cold in winter. The only advantage of this means of transport is the cost. It is very cheap. But you only pay for what you get!

GRAMMAR

1 Write *a* or *an* in front of these words. Then write the plurals of the words.

an appointment appointments

1 _____ bus __________
2 _____ coach __________
3 _____ ferry __________
4 _____ airport __________
5 _____ house __________
6 _____ office __________
7 _____ delay __________
8 _____ hour __________

2 Complete the sentences with *a/an* or *the* or put - if there is no article.

1 _____ number eighteen bus stops in _____ centre of town.
2 I go to _____ work by bus.
3 He works eight hours _____ day.
4 She lives and works in _____ Milan.
5 Helen is _____ secretary.
6 She works at _____ Continental tourist office near Victoria Station.
7 He takes _____ taxi twice _____ week.
8 _____ plane to Chicago leaves at seven.
9 I stay at _____ home on Thursdays.
10 She always goes to _____ office by _____ bicycle.

3 Write questions for these answers.

1 ______________________________
It takes about an hour.
2 ______________________________
I go by car.
3 ______________________________
No, I only go twice a month.
4 ______________________________
Fifty pence.
5 ______________________________
It's about thirty miles.

SOUNDS

1 Listen and underline the word links.

1 It's about eighty miles.
2 The office is near the station.
3 It's the age of the train.
4 It's quite expensive.
5 People sit on the roof.

Listen again and repeat.

2 Match the words with the same vowel sounds.

slow	ride
train	live
bus	coach
drive	long
stop	plane
quick	month

Now listen and check your answers.

WRITING

1 Look back at the *Reading* passage in your Student's Book. Do you agree that now is *the age of the train*? If not, complete the sentence below with another word. Explain your opinion in a few lines.

It's the age of the __________.

____
____
____
____
____

2 Write a few lines describing these means of transport in your country.

taxis

____
____

trains

____
____

buses and coaches

____
____

13 *Can you swim?*

VOCABULARY AND GRAMMAR

1 Complete the crossword. You can look in your Student's Book to help you.

Across
3 You do this in water.
6 You can do this in a kitchen.
8 You can't eat water, you _____ it.
9 Infinitive of *am*.
12 *Does* in the 1st person.
13 What you do on a horse.
17 You need a book or a magazine to do this.
18 To be first in a race you _____.
19 Pigs can't do this, nor can chickens, but planes can.

Down
1 You can't do it in the summer.
2 To have something in your hand.
4 To go on foot.
5 They _____ their friends at the club on Sundays.
7 To make a sweater.
10 Don't stop.
11 What you do with a car.
14 To make a picture.
15 You _____ a meal.
16 Can you _____ a musical instrument?
17 I can't _____ 100 metres in 15 seconds.

2 Complete the sentences with *can* or *can't*.

1 I __________ do crosswords at all.
2 He __________ knit quite well.
3 They __________ speak English very well, but they __________ write it.
4 She __________ swim, but not very fast.
5 I __________ dance quite well, but I __________ cook at all.

3 Write five sentences about what you *can* or *can't do*. Use *very well*, *quite well* and *not at all*.

1 ______________________________
2 ______________________________
3 ______________________________
4 ______________________________
5 ______________________________

4 Write a suitable question or a sentence.

1 ______________________________
Yes, I can.
2 ______________________________
Nor can I.
3 ______________________________
No, I can't.
4 ______________________________
So can I.

SOUNDS

1 Listen and underline the letters which are not pronounced.

cupboard daylight foreign hour knit listen night often walk write

Listen again and repeat.

2 Listen and put a tick (✓) if the underlined sound is /æ/ and a cross (x) if it is /ə/.

1 I can speak English fluently.
2 Can you drive a car?
3 I can cook quite well.
4 So can I.
5 I can play the guitar.
6 Yes, I can!

Listen and repeat.

READING AND WRITING

1 Write the names of these objects in the spaces.

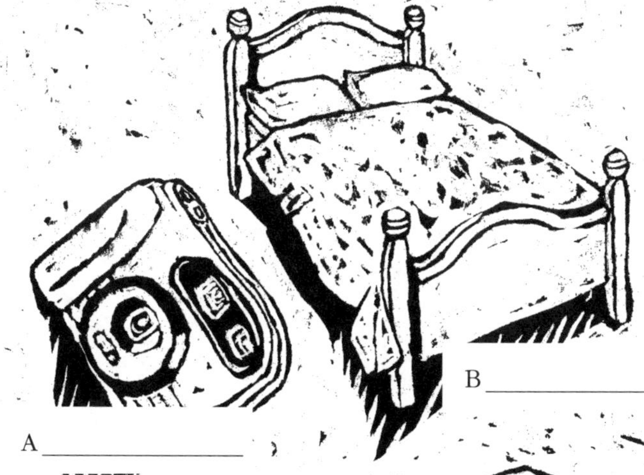

A ______________

B ______________

C ______________

D ______________

E ______________

F ______________

2 Match the descriptions with the objects in the pictures.

1 This is a machine. It can wash plates. It is usually in the kitchen.
2 It is often upstairs in a house. You can sleep in it or just lie on it.
3 This is often in the sitting room. You can put it on and watch a programme. You can also use it to watch a video.
4 This thing can take pictures. It is not very big and you can carry it in your bag.
5 It is often in the sitting room. It is hot. You can sit in front of it when you are cold.
6 If you look in it you can see yourself. It can be on a wall in any room of the house. There is always one in the bathroom.

3 Circle all the verbs in the descriptions in activity 2. Check that you understand their meanings.

4 Underline the words that say where the objects usually are.

5 Write similar descriptions for these objects.

a radio

____

____

a car

____

____

a mobile phone

____

____

14 How do I get to Queen Street?

VOCABULARY

1 Circle the verbs in the box.

meal suncream stamps send lamp clothes account medicine eat menu cassette buy magazine platform aspirin dinner money newspaper sweets ticket traveller's cheques letters take out train envelopes change

2 Match the words in the box with these places. There are some extra words.

post office *stamps* ________

newsagent's ________

chemist's ________

bank ________

station ________

restaurant ________

3 Write a sentence for each of the places in activity 2.

You can buy stamps in a post office.

1 ________

2 ________

3 ________

4 ________

5 ________

6 ________

GRAMMAR AND READING

1 Read the description of Hereford town centre. Check that you understand the underlined words.

2 Underline all the prepositions of place.

3 Put the following places on the map.

museum shopping mall bank
tourist information centre chemist's post office
indoor market park hotel

Hereford is a small market town in the west of England. The High Street is very short with a big square at the end of it called High Town. There are a lot of attractive shops in High Town and there are no cars. You can visit the beautiful Old House which is a museum in the middle of High Town. There is a post office behind the Old House opposite the bookshop. There is a bank with a cash machine opposite the library in Broad Street. There is an indoor food market in High Town between Gromond Street and Widemarsh Street. Behind the market is a small shopping mall called Maylord Orchards. There is a big chemist's shop in the High Street opposite the newsagent's. At the end of Church Street there is a small park and the cathedral. In Broad Street, on the same side of the road as the library, is a very good hotel and restaurant called The Green Dragon.
The tourist information office is on the corner of Broad Street and King Street opposite the library. Wednesday is market day and the town is very busy. There is a big market out of the town centre where you can buy all sorts of things. There is also a cattle market where they sell cows, sheep and pigs.

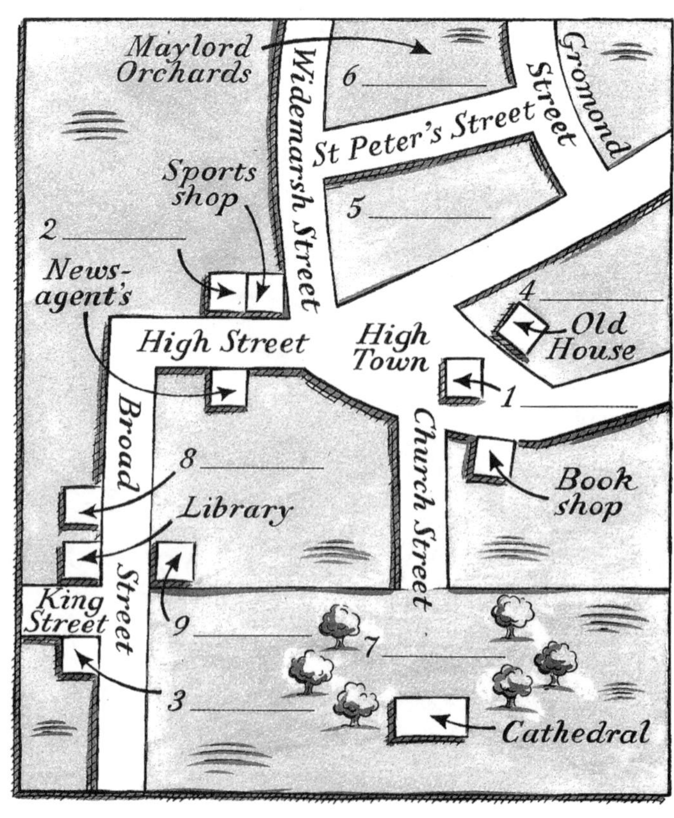

4 Look at the map of the town centre and complete the sentences with a preposition of place.

1 The tourist information centre is __________ the library.
2 The museum is in High Town __________ the post office and the bookshop.
3 The newsagent's is __________ the chemist's.
4 The library is __________ Broad Street and King Street.
5 The shopping mall is __________ the indoor market.
6 The sports shop is __________ the chemist's and __________ the newsagent's.

LISTENING

1 Look at the map and listen to three conversations which take place at the tourist information centre. What do the people want?

Conversation 1 ______________________________
Conversation 2 ______________________________
Conversation 3 ______________________________

2 Listen to Conversations 1 and 2 again and complete the directions.

Conversation 1

1 Go __________ Broad Street.
2 Turn __________ into the High Street, then __________ __________ into High Town.
3 The post office is __________ the bookshop, __________ the Old House.

Conversation 2

1 Walk __________ Broad Street.
2 The chemist's is __________ the newsagent's.
3 It's __________ __________ __________ of a sports shop.

3 Listen to Conversation 3 again and underline anything that is different from what you hear.

A Hello, Peter. How are you?
B Fine, thanks. Why are you here in town?
A I'm with my husband. We are looking for a nice place to have a meal. Can you tell me where there is a good French restaurant?
B Yes. There's a restaurant called Pasta in Widemarsh Street. It has a good reputation.
A How can I get to Widemarsh Street from here? Is it far?
B No. About twenty minutes' walk. Go down Broad Street. Turn right into the High Street, then turn left into Widemarsh Street. Go along there for about ten metres and the restaurant is on the right, next to the baker's. There's an Italian restaurant on the same side of the road.
A Thanks. Bye.

WRITING

1 Complete the dialogue.

A ______________________________
B At the vegetable market.
A ______________________________
B No, it's very near. It's only about five minutes' walk from here.
A ______________________________
B Yes. You go along the High Street until you get to the square. The entrance to the market is on your left next to a big shoe shop.
A ______________________________
B The vegetable shops are inside the market on the left.
A ______________________________
B Yes. There are two florist's at the opposite end of the market hall.
A ______________________________

2 Choose three places in your town or village. Write directions from your home to the places.

____
____
____
____
____

15 What's happening?

GRAMMAR

1 Write the present participles of these verbs.

enjoy *enjoying*
stay ________
pass ________
have ________
live ________
learn ________
shop ________
sit ________
fly ________
travel ________
take ________
lie ________
write ________

2 Complete the sentences with verbs in the present continuous. Choose from the list in activity 1.

1 We ____________ in a very cheap hotel on the coast.
2 She ____________ on the beach in the sun.
3 They ____________ dinner outside.
4 We ____________ at 10,000 metres.
5 I hope you ____________ the flight.

3 Write six sentences in the present continuous with verbs from the list in activity 1.

1 ______________________________
2 ______________________________
3 ______________________________
4 ______________________________
5 ______________________________
6 ______________________________

SOUNDS

1 How many syllables are there in these words? Put them in the correct list. Underline the stressed syllables.

beautiful attractive ugly industrial lively modern mountains wonderful boring

Two syllables ______________________________

____

Three syllables ______________________________

____

Four syllables ______________________________

____

Listen and check. Say the words aloud.

2 Listen and underline the stressed words.

1 We're having a wonderful time.
2 I'm not enjoying the flight.
3 She's learning to swim.
4 They're staying at an expensive hotel.
5 He's travelling for his job.
6 I'm writing this on the beach.

Listen and repeat.

VOCABULARY

Write the opposites of these adjectives. You can use your dictionary.

beautiful *ugly*
east ________
interesting ________
old-fashioned ________
north ________
cold ________
dark ________
quiet ________

LISTENING

1 Look at the photos. Which words can you use to describe the places?

chalet modern sea old coast skiing industrial mountains river town snow port cold holiday

2 Write down two or three words or expressions to describe each place in the photos.

Picture A ______________________

Picture B ______________________

Picture C ______________________

3 Listen to two telephone conversations. Which two places in the photos are the people phoning from?

Conversation 1 ______________________

Conversation 2 ______________________

4 Listen again. Are these sentences true or false?

Conversation 1

1 Anna is phoning her husband.
2 She's staying in a hotel outside the city.
3 She's having a wonderful time.
4 It's raining at the moment.

Conversation 2

1 Stephie is phoning her father.
2 She's staying in a hotel in the mountains.
3 She's having a holiday with her parents.
4 Her parents are visiting the town at the moment.

READING AND WRITING

1 Read the description of Monaco. Underline the expressions which describe where Monaco is.

2 Why does Monaco attract people? Find five things.

MONACO is the world's second smallest country after the Vatican. There are only 30,000 inhabitants. It is on the Mediterranean coast in the south-east of France near Italy. Monaco-Ville is the capital. Many tourists visit Monaco because of its beautiful location between the mountains and the sea and also because of its pleasant climate. Others go there for the gambling casinos or to see the famous Formula 1 motor race. Many rich people from different countries live in Monaco because there are no taxes.

3 Write a paragraph describing a city you know. Say why it is attractive.

16 *Who was your first friend?*

VOCABULARY AND READING

1 Read the passages and decide where these sentences go.

a My first holiday without my parents was in Greece.
b It was the worst holiday I can remember.
c She was my first girlfriend.
d My first pet was a dog.

2 Who or what do these words and expressions describe in the passages?

noisy shy horrid exciting dark wonderful not well-behaved naughty attractive hot bad-tempered terrible not obedient

■ (1) **His name was Toby.** He was a small, brown dog with a long tail. He was noisy and often quite naughty and he wasn't at all obedient. But he was my best friend when I was a child and we were always together.

■ (2) **I was seventeen years old.** It was very exciting because it was the first time I was not with my parents. There were four of us. We were all good friends from the same school. It was in August and we were there for two weeks. I remember it was very hot. It was a wonderful holiday and one of my best memories.

■ **She was very shy and very attractive.** She wasn't very tall and she had long, dark hair. We were at the same school but we weren't in the same class. She was good at music and art and I was good at languages and maths. We were both fourteen years old and we were always together. (3)

■ **I remember that holiday very well because it was terrible.** I was in a caravan by the sea for a week with my parents and two brothers. The weather was horrid. Every day it was cold and wet. There wasn't one sunny day during the week. Because there was nothing to do we weren't very well-behaved and our parents were bad-tempered. It was good to get back home. (4)

GRAMMAR

1 Complete these sentences with *was* or *were*.

1 She __________ late for work this morning.
2 They __________ in London last week.
3 I __________ at home yesterday.
4 We __________ at the restaurant last night.
5 You __________ with your brother yesterday.
6 The weather __________ very wet last month.

2 Put the words in order and write questions.

1 were where born you?

______

2 like were you school what at?

______

3 friend at was who school your best?

______

4 at you good were what?

______

5 trouble often were school you at in?

______

3 Answer the questions in activity 2.

1 ______
2 ______
3 ______
4 ______
5 ______

4 Answer these questions about yesterday.

1 What day was it?

______

2 What was the weather like?

______

3 Where were you in the morning?

______

4 Were you alone or with other people?

______

VOCABULARY AND SOUNDS

1 Underline the stressed syllables in these words.

stubborn obedient lazy cheerful horrid
untidy polite naughty disappointing

2 Write down someone or something you can use these adjectives to describe.

______
______
______
______
______

3 Listen and repeat the questions in *Grammar* activity 2.

LISTENING

1 Listen to a conversation. Number the questions in the right order.

a Where were you? ☐
b How was your holiday? ☐
c Were you in a good hotel? ☐
d What about the food? ☐
e What was the weather like? ☐
f Who were you with? ☐

2 Answer the questions in activity 1 about your last holiday.

1 ______
2 ______
3 ______
4 ______
5 ______
6 ______

WRITING

Look at the passages in *Vocabulary and Reading* again. Write a similar passage about one of these topics.

your first boy/girlfriend your first pet
your first holiday without your parents
your worst/best family holiday

______
______
______
______
______
______
______
______
______
______

17 How about some oranges?

VOCABULARY

1 Circle the odd-word-out.

1 beef rice pork lamb chicken
2 butter cheese milk bacon yoghurt
3 potato banana apple orange grape
4 water wine juice milk oil
5 knife fork plate salt spoon
6 meat onion vegetables fruit drink

2 Write down the names of three typical dishes from your country. Make a list of some of the ingredients in these dishes.

____
____
____
____
____

READING AND WRITING

1 Read the passage. Are these sentences true or false?

1 They sometimes sit on the floor when they eat.
2 They often use chopsticks.
3 They don't use their fingers.
4 They can't drink alcohol in public.
5 Smoking is common.
6 They don't put salt on the table.
7 They eat early in the evening.
8 Restaurants are very formal.

2 Read the passage again and find out what is:

informal *eating habits*
common ______________________________
____
crowded, noisy and hot ______________________________
____
relaxed ______________________________
____

3 Are the underlined words in the passage countables or uncountables? Write *C* or *U* above each word.

4 Correct the false sentences in activity 1.

1 ______________________________
2 ______________________________
3 ______________________________
4 ______________________________

Eating habits are very informal. You sit at a table or in a circle on the floor around the food. All the food is put out on different plates at the start of the meal. You take what you want. Most people eat with a spoon and a fork. You can use your fingers to make rice balls which you dip in various sauces. Chopsticks are only common with the Chinese population in Thailand. There isn't usually any salt because they use fish sauce.

Thais can eat and drink anything. There are no social taboos. Drinking alcohol is a normal social activity for men. Smoking is common among men and women.

Thais eat early in the evening. They usually have their evening meal at about six o'clock. Most traditional Thai restaurants close at about eight o'clock. So if you go early, it is crowded, noisy and hot and if you go late there is no food left! These restaurants are very relaxed. You can even take your own drink into a Thai restaurant!

GRAMMAR AND LISTENING

1 Write *C* for a countable or *U* for an uncountable.

wine	____	apple	____	oil	____
yoghurt	____	egg	____	butter	____
onion	____	pork	____	lemon	____
milk	____	carrot	____	water	____
beef	____	bread	____	tea	____
salt	____	rice	____	soup	____
steak	____	pasta	____	cheese	____

2 Complete the gaps with *some*, *any* or *a/an*.

1 We need __________ mineral water.
2 Let's have __________ fruit.
3 Can I have __________ banana, please?
4 I'm sorry. We haven't got __________ bananas.
5 How about __________ pasta?
6 I need __________ cup of coffee.

3 Look at the dialogue below. What is the situation?

____

4 Complete the dialogue with *some*, *any* or *a/an*.

Listen and check.

A I'd like (1) __________ vegetable soup with bread, please

B I'm afraid we haven't got (2) __________ soup today, madam. But we've got (3) __________ potato salad.

A I don't like salads. I'll have (4) __________ cheese omelette.

B Cheese omelette. And for the main course?

A Roast chicken with boiled potatoes.

B I'm sorry, but we haven't got (5) __________ chicken. But you can have (6) __________ steak. And there is pasta or chips instead of boiled potatoes.

A All right. A steak and chips. Have you got (7) __________ wine or is there only water or tea?

B Of course, madam. We've got (8) __________ good Bulgarian red wine.

A Haven't you got (9) __________ white wine?

B Yes. It's German.

A That's fine. And cheese. I'd like (10) __________ cheese and (11) __________ ice cream.

B Do you want (12) __________ water?

A Yes, please. A bottle of spring water.

WRITING

1 Look at the picture of a wedding reception in Britain. Write a few sentences describing the situation.

____
____
____
____
____
____
____
____
____
____

2 Describe a typical wedding feast in your country.

____
____
____
____
____
____
____
____
____
____

18 I was born in England

VOCABULARY

1 Match these words with the definitions.

album award group guitar hit musician piano singer teenager

1. a very popular song or piece of music __________
2. a young person __________
3. a collection of songs or pieces of music __________
4. someone who plays an instrument __________
5. more than one musician __________
6. something a singer can receive when he or she sells a lot of records __________
7. most pop groups have one or more of these instruments __________

2 Match the two parts of the sentence. You can look in your Student's Book.

1	She was born	a	in the film *The Bodyguard*.
2	He created	b	a hit with her first album.
3	She appeared	c	to sing on his own in 1984.
4	She received	d	the group *The Police* in 1978.
5	He started	e	as a teacher in Newcastle.
6	He played	f	an award for a song.
7	He worked	g	in New Jersey in 1964.
8	She had	h	the piano and the guitar.

GRAMMAR AND READING

1 Write the past simple of these verbs.

appear	__________	marry	__________
create	__________	move	__________
die	__________	play	__________
learn	__________	start	__________
live	__________	work	__________
compose	__________	finish	__________

2 Complete the sentences with a verb in the past simple from the list in activity 1.

1. Sting __________ Trudy Styler in 1986.
2. Whitney Houston __________ in *The Bodyguard.*
3. As a child he __________ to play the piano and guitar.
4. As a teenager she __________ with rhythm and blues singers.
5. Sting __________ to sing on his own in 1984.
6. Sting __________ the group *The Police.*

3 Read the passage about Mozart and complete the gaps with verbs in the past simple from activity 1.

Mozart was born in 1756 in Austria. As a child he (1) __________ to play the harpsichord, the violin and the piano. When he was five years old he (2) __________ writing music. He (3) __________ in public all over Europe before he was ten. He (4) __________ in Italy from 1768 to 1771. In 1771 he (5) __________ to Salzburg and organized concerts there. In 1781 he (6) __________ to Vienna and he (7) __________ Constanze Weber, a singer. In 1786 he created his first important opera, *The Marriage of Figaro*. In the following year he (8) __________ as the official court musician to Joseph II. In 1788 he (9) __________ his three last symphonies. Mozart (10) __________ a poor man at the age of 35.

SOUNDS

1 Circle the word in each line with a different-sounding ending.

1. lived opened talked played received
2. worked appeared looked liked finished
3. enjoyed died loved visited married
4. decided started wanted created watched

Listen and check.

2 Listen and underline the stressed words.

1 She was born in London.
2 He learned to play the piano.
3 She received an award.
4 They created the group *The Police.*
5 He started work as a teacher.

Listen again and repeat.

LISTENING

1 Do you know the stars in the pictures? Write a few words about each one.

1 Kevin Costner

____

____

2 Jodie Foster

____

____

3 Elton John

____

____

Kevin Costner
Elton John
Jodie Foster

2 Listen to conversations about two of the stars. Who are they about?

Conversation 1 ______________________________

Conversation 2 ______________________________

3 Listen to Conversation 1 again and complete the sentences.

1 He ______________ in Los Angeles in 1955.
2 He ______________ business at the University of California.
3 He ______________ an Oscar for his film *Dances with Wolves.*
4 He ______________ in the film *The Bodyguard* with Whitney Houston.
5 He ______________ in *Robin Hood.*

4 Listen to Conversation 2 again and take notes about:

when she was born ______________________________

her nationality ______________________________

where she studied ______________________________

her film career ______________________________

WRITING

1 Use your notes in *Listening* activity 4 to write a description of Jodie Foster.

____

____

____

____

____

2 Use the information below to write about Elton John.

Birth place: *Middlesex, England*
Date of birth: *1947*
As a child: *piano lessons*
Work: *pianist in the 1960s*
Hits: *between 1972 and 1980 40 hits in the USA*
Concerts: *first western star to play in Moscow*
Image: *extraordinary glasses*

____

____

____

____

____

19 What's he like?

VOCABULARY

1 Write down adjectives you can use to describe a person's:

hair ______________________

____

body build ______________________

____

personality ______________________

____

age ______________________

____

2 Look at the pictures and read the descriptions. Underline things that are not correct.

3 Correct the descriptions in activity 2. Write sentences.

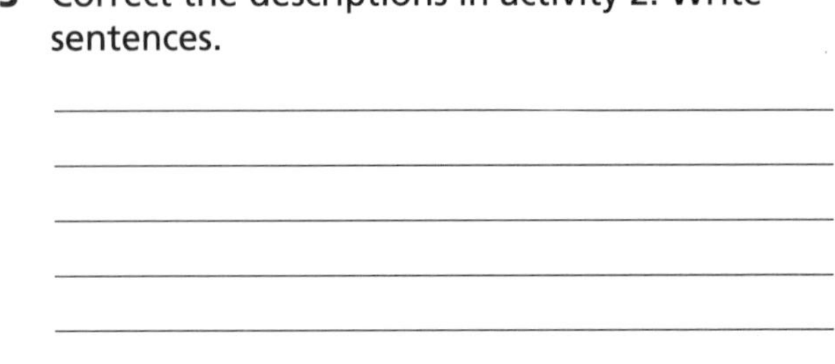

C *She's an elderly woman with an attractive face. She's fair with very short, curly hair. She's not very tall and she's got glasses.*

A *She is about thirty-five years old. She's about one metre sixty-five. She's quite slim and very attractive. She's got long, curly hair. She's got glasses.*

B *He's middle-aged and rather good-looking. He's very tall and well-built. He's dark with short, straight hair.*

FUNCTIONS

1 Write questions for these answers.

1 ______________________________

He's very nice.

2 ______________________________

She's medium-height and she's got long, fair hair.

3 ______________________________

She's one metre sixty-five.

4 ______________________________

He's fifty-two.

5 ______________________________

She looks like her mother.

6 ______________________________

She usually wears fashionable clothes.

2 Answer the questions about yourself.

1 ______________________________
2 ______________________________
3 ______________________________
4 ______________________________
5 ______________________________
6 ______________________________

SOUNDS

Listen and say these words aloud.

built kind slim time nice thin smile polite sixty child

Is the vowel sound /ɪ/ or /aɪ/? Put the words in two groups.

/ɪ/: ______________________________

/aɪ/: ______________________________

LISTENING

1 Listen to three descriptions. Who are the speakers describing? Put the number of the description by the person.

a new baby ☐ a criminal ☐ a new boss ☐
an old classmate ☐ a lost child ☐

2 Listen to Description 1 again and complete the sentences.

1 He's about __________ years old.
2 He's got __________, __________ hair.
3 He's wearing a __________ sweater, __________ shorts and __________ trainers.

3 Listen to Description 2 again and tick (✓) the sentences which describe the woman's appearance now.

1 She's small with long, dark hair.
2 She's tall and slim.
3 She wears glasses.
4 She is very hard working.
5 She's very quiet and polite.
6 She wears very smart clothes.

4 Listen to Description 3 again and take notes. Write a short description of the man.

____
____
____
____
____

WRITING

Write a description of two members of your family.

____
____
____
____
____
____
____
____
____

20 A grand tour

VOCABULARY

1 Find 15 irregular past verbs in the puzzle. They go (→) and (↓).

F	D	I	D	M	A	D	E
O	G	B	O	U	G	H	T
U	A	C	T	O	O	K	W
N	V	A	S	A	I	D	R
D	E	M	L	O	S	T	O
H	G	E	W	E	N	T	T
A	O	S	P	E	N	T	E
D	T	B	E	C	A	M	E

2 Complete the sentences with words from the puzzle.

1 I __________ a postcard to my parents.
2 He __________ some shopping at the supermarket.
3 They __________ to Florence for the weekend.
4 She __________ a train from Florence to Rome.
5 We __________ some new friends at the hotel.
6 I haven't got a passport now because I __________ it when I was on holiday.

3 Match the two parts of the sentences.

1	She went	a	at home last night.
2	They found	b	to Rome for her holiday.
3	I bought	c	on the beach all afternoon.
4	We stayed	d	the Queen when she was in London.
5	He lay	e	a cheap hotel near the station.
6	She saw	f	some drinks.

GRAMMAR

1 Put the words in order and write questions.

1 yesterday visit did a you museum?
____
2 you some the did write at postcards weekend?
____
3 did do you shopping yesterday some?
____
4 Saturday you a to restaurant go on did?
____
5 you take a week did train last?
____

2 Answer the questions in activity 1 with a short answer.

1 __________
2 __________
3 __________
4 __________
5 __________

3 Write suitable questions.

Did she go to Italy last week?
Yes, she did. She went with a friend.
1 __________
No, I didn't. I went to a restaurant.
2 __________
No, we didn't. We stayed at home.
3 __________
Yes, we did. I bought some new clothes.
4 __________
Yes, he did. He enjoyed it very much.

READING

1 Look quickly at the letter and find answers to these questions.

1 Who is writing?

____

2 Who is she writing to?

____

3 Is she travelling alone?

____

2 Read the letter. Correct these statements.

1 The weather was cold in London.

____

2 She spent a week in London.

____

3 She flew to Paris.

____

4 She found a cheap hotel in the Latin Quarter.

____

5 She lost her bag in a taxi.

____

6 She went to Florence after Paris.

____

7 She stayed with her cousin in Barcelona.

____

8 She spent a day by the sea near Barcelona.

____

14th May 1997

Dear Robert,

This is our third week here in Europe and we're having a great time. The people are very friendly and the weather is good – even in Britain it was sunny and warm!

We flew to London from Montreal and we spent four days visiting the city. There's so much to see and do! Unfortunately we didn't see the Queen! Mike was very disappointed!

Then we took the Eurostar to Paris and we stayed with my cousin, Angie. We did some sightseeing and we visited the Louvre and the Eiffel Tower, of course. We had some wonderful food in small restaurants in the Latin Quarter. I lost my passport in the Metro so we went to the Canadian Embassy to get another.

After Paris we flew to Barcelona where it was very hot. We made friends with some local people in a bar and they showed us the city. We took a bus to a small town on the coast and we found a hotel with a beautiful view of the sea. We relaxed on the beach for two days before moving on to Italy where we are now. We arrived here in Florence early this morning and we're having a big breakfast before we go sightseeing.

After Florence, we are going to Rome, Athens and then Istanbul. I'll write again in two weeks' time.

Give my love to Anne and the children.

See you soon!

Diana

SOUNDS

Circle the word in each line with a different vowel sound.

1 lose good shoes blue you
2 close won love come some
3 got was lost born what
4 write fly find give buy
5 stay have take gave made

Listen and say the words aloud.

21 Mystery

GRAMMAR AND VOCABULARY

1 Write the past simple of these verbs. Underline the irregular verbs.

encourage *encouraged*
inform ______
think ______
sell ______
marry ______
leave ______
find ______
refuse ______

2 Match the two parts of the sentences. You can look back at your Student's Book.

1	Her mother encouraged	a	to write her mysteries.
2	She married	b	the famous writer was dead.
3	She disappeared	c	her to read.
4	The police informed	d	Colonel Archibald Christie.
5	Everyone thought	e	for 11 days.
6	She continued	f	what happened in 1962.
7	She didn't explain	g	the newspapers of her disappearance.

3 Write down five things that you *didn't do* yesterday.

I didn't go to the cinema.

1 ______
2 ______
3 ______
4 ______
5 ______

SOUNDS

1 How many syllables are there in these words? Put them in the correct list.

continue disappear divorced encourage explain famous final happen inform notice refuse successful

Two syllables ______

______

Three syllables ______

______

2 Underline the stressed syllables in the words in activity 1.

Listen and check. Say the words aloud.

He was born in 1564 in Stratford-upon-Avon. He was the son of a Stratford businessman and went to the local grammar school. In 1582 he married Anne Hathaway. They had three children. We know that he left Stratford in about 1585. But no one knows where he went or what he did for the next five years. In September 1592 we know that he lived and worked in London as a playwright and as an actor at the Globe Theatre. He is not on the actor-list after 1603 so he probably stopped acting at this time because he was already famous for his writing.

He wrote his first play, *Henry VI*, in 1590–91. He also wrote a large number of poems. He finished his last play, *The Tempest*, in 1612. After that he left London and went back to live in Stratford. He died in 1616. His plays are very successful today.

READING

1 Read the biography of a famous English writer. Can you guess who he is? Underline all the verbs in the past simple.

2 Write questions about the writer.

1 Where/born?
Where was he born?
2 When/born?
______
3 Where/go to school?
______
4 Who/marry?
______
5 Where/work as an actor?
______
6 When/stop acting?
______
7 Why/stop acting?
______
8 When/write his first play?
______
9 Where/go in 1612?
______
10 When/die?
______

3 What years of his life are a mystery to us today?

______

4 Answer the questions in activity 2.

1 ______
2 ______
3 ______
4 ______
5 ______
6 ______
7 ______
8 ______
9 ______
10 ______

WRITING

1 Complete the biography of Doris Lessing, a successful writer, with verbs from the list.

be go live receive win write

Doris Lessing ______ born of British parents in Iran in 1919 and ______ to live in Zimbabwe when she ______ five. As a child she ______ on a large farm and first ______ to England in 1949. She ______ her first novel, *The Grass is Singing*, in 1950. It ______ a great success in Britain and the United States. She ______ an award for her collection of short stories, *Five*.

2 Use the information below to write the biography of another famous writer. Can you guess who he/she is?

born Missouri USA 1835
ship's pilot on the Mississippi in 1857
journalist in 1862 tour of Europe 1865
The Adventures of Tom Sawyer in 1876
death 1910

______
______
______
______
______
______
______
______
______
______

22 Dates

VOCABULARY AND SOUNDS

1 Write the words for the following numbers.

4th	*fourth*	9th	________
5th	________	12th	________
6th	________	13th	________
8th	________	15th	________

Listen and repeat.

2 Write one or more nouns from these verbs. You can use your dictionary.

Verb	**Noun**
discover	________
explode	________
invent	________
land	________
paint	________
take off	________
win	________

3 Complete the sentences with a verb from activity 2.

1 Brazil ________ the World Cup in 1962.
2 Fleming ________ penicillin in 1928.
3 The first atom bomb ________ in 1945.
4 Picasso ________ *Guernica* in 1937.
5 Alfred Nobel ________ dynamite in 1866.
6 The first astronauts ________ on the moon on 20th July 1969.

READING

1 Read the passage below. Choose the best picture to illustrate the passage.

2 What happened on the following dates?

12th April 1981 ________________
January 1986 ________________
25th April 1990 ________________
May 1992 ________________

The US space organisation, NASA
(*National Aeronautics and Space Administration*) developed and built the first space shuttle. The shuttle was the first rocket to fly into space, come back to earth and fly again. The first shuttle to fly in space was *Columbia*. It took off on the 12th April 1981. In January 1986 the shuttle *Challenger* exploded at take-off. Everyone on the shuttle died. This accident slowed down the shuttle programme for the next six years. A new shuttle, *Endeavor*, replaced *Challenger* in May 1992.

On 25th April 1990, NASA used the shuttle *Discovery* to put the Hubble Space Telescope into space at a distance of 512 kilometres from the earth. Hubble travels around the earth and sends back photos of the stars and planets.

A

B

GRAMMAR

1 Match a word from Box A with a word from Box B to form an expression of past time. You can add an article if necessary.

A	B
in on at yesterday last ago	Friday month weekend June night week 1995 10 years evening 26th March morning

in June

2 Answer the questions in two ways.

When did you last visit a museum?

I last visited a museum in March.

I last visited a museum two months ago.

1 When did you last lose something?

2 When did you last eat an egg?

3 When did you last run 100 metres?

4 When did you last sing in the bath?

5 When did you last see a funny film?

3 Write four more questions with *when*.

1 ______

2 ______

3 ______

4 ______

4 Write about things you did:

1 last week

2 three weeks ago

3 last night

4 on Saturday

5 yesterday morning

6 a few minutes ago

LISTENING

Listen and complete the dialogue with expressions of time.

MAN By the way, do you remember Janet Finch? She was at school with us.

WOMAN Yes, of course! What about her?

MAN I met her (1) ______ at the supermarket.

WOMAN Oh, how is she? The last time I saw her was (2) ______.

MAN She looked very well. She lived in Italy from (3) ______ to (4) ______. She was a teacher in Milan.

WOMAN When did she come back to Britain?

MAN (5) ______. She spent (6) ______ in Coventry, then she moved to Cambridge (7) ______.

WRITING

Write about four or five memorable events that took place in your life in the last two years.

I went to university last September.

23 What's she wearing?

VOCABULARY

1 Complete the crossword.

Across
1 The top part of a suit.
6 A casual top for everyone (two words).
8 One on each foot.
9 Only a woman wears this.
11 A woman's shirt.

Down
1 Casual trousers.
2 You need this in winter.
3 All men and some women wear them.
4 Summer clothes.
5 Jacket and trousers the same colour.
7 Footwear for winter.
8 You put it on before your shoe.
10 Very smart round a man's neck.

2 Make a list of clothes you have got which are:

comfortable *an old T-shirt*
warm __________
fashionable __________
smart __________
casual __________

LISTENING

1 Look at the models in the pictures. Write the names of the clothes they are wearing in the spaces.

2 Listen to the fashion show commentary. Put the number of the commentary in the correct box.

3 Listen again and write the colours of the clothes in the spaces.

4 Choose one of the models and write a description of her outfit.

____

5 Write a description of an outfit you have.

____

READING AND GRAMMAR

1 Read the letter and find the answers to these questions.

1 Who is writing to who?

____

2 Where is the writer?

____

3 Who is Aunt Grace?

____

2 Underline four verbs in the present continuous and circle four verbs in the present simple.

3 Find these adjectives in the letter. What or who do they describe?

expensive ______________
wonderful ______________
beautiful ______________
lovely ______________
interesting ______________
happy ______________

Dear Sarah,
I'm having a wonderful holiday here in New Zealand. I'm staying in Wellington with my Aunt Grace – she's my mother's cousin. Aunt Grace is 58 years old.
She's a small lady with short, dark hair. She's got lovely brown eyes and she wears round glasses. She smiles all the time and she talks non-stop. She is very interesting because she reads a lot. She came to live in New Zealand when she was 25. She doesn't know any of her nephews and nieces back home because she never goes to Britain. She says it's too far and too expensive and she's very happy where she is.
She's a chief gardener in a big city park, but she's having a holiday this week because I'm staying with her. Every day we visit somewhere different. The scenery is beautiful in the mountains. I'm staying here for two weeks, then I'm flying to Australia for another three weeks.
See you soon,
Love,
Pat

4 Choose the correct tense.

1 We *stay/are staying* in an expensive hotel by the sea.
2 They *live/are living* in Milan in the winter.
3 He usually *wears/is wearing* smart clothes.
4 She *is looking/looks* for a new flat at the moment.
5 He *goes/is going* to work by car every day.
6 She *laughs/is laughing* because he said something funny.

WRITING

Describe yourself and what you are wearing at the moment. Use the present continuous.

I'm wearing comfortable shoes ...

24 *I'm going to save money*

VOCABULARY

1 Complete the sentences with these verbs.

save stop spend study worry invite

1 I'm going to __________ at Oxford University.
2 I'm going to __________ smoking.
3 I'm not going to __________ about my work anymore.
4 We're going to __________ money to buy a house.
5 I'm not going to __________ so much money on clothes.
6 I'm going to __________ friends for dinner on Saturday.

2 Match the two parts of the sentences.

1	They're going to travel	a	to him.
2	I'm looking forward	b	in a few minutes.
3	She studied	c	together.
4	It's going to leave	d	around the world.
5	She waved goodbye	e	very hard at school.
6	They grew up	f	to seeing her again.

GRAMMAR

1 Look at the pictures and say what the people are going to do.

1 ______________________________
2 ______________________________
3 ______________________________
4 ______________________________

2 Complete the plans with suitable reasons.

1 I'm going to change my job
because I don't enjoy it.
2 I'm going to buy a bicycle
____
3 He's going to save money
____
4 We're going to go running once a week
____
5 She's going to spend more time at home
____

3 Write intentions. Use *so*.

He is very ambitious
so he is going to find a more important job.

1 I can't swim
____
2 Jane doesn't know anyone here
____
3 They don't like living in the city centre
____
4 We don't know the USA
____
5 I'm saving a thousand pounds
____

4 Write sentences about things that you are definitely not going to do this week. Say why.

____
____
____
____
____
____

SOUNDS

1 Listen and put a tick (✓) by the sentences where *to* is pronounced /tuː/ and a cross (x) where it is pronounced /tə/.

1 We're going to see a film.
2 She's going to eat at home tonight.
3 I'm going to work on my own.
4 We're going to invite friends for dinner.
5 I'm going to get fit.

Listen again and repeat. Notice how the final *g* of *going* is not pronounced.

2 Listen and notice how the underlined consonants are said together as one sound.

1 she found time
2 next door
3 played together
4 went to the same school
5 spend time
6 I need to

Listen again and repeat.

LISTENING

1 Listen to a conversation about future plans. What is the conversation about?

a moving to a new home
b planning a business trip
c retirement plans

2 Listen again and complete the sentences.

1 Chris is __________ years old.
2 He doesn't __________ for the building company any more because he is retired.
3 Betty and Chris are going on a two-month __________.
4 They're going to ____________________.
5 They're not going to __________ to the country, they're going to stay in __________.
6 They're going to move to a small __________ near the __________.

WRITING

1 Look at the page from a working woman's agenda. What job do you think she does?

saleswoman magazine fashion writer
interpreter hat designer

Monday	2 pm Visit the hat exhibition at the new art and design college
Tuesday	7.15 am Eurostar to Paris 11 am Interview with Paris clothes designer
Wednesday	Editorial meeting for January edition
Thursday	Piccadilly clothes show
Friday	Finish article on hats
Saturday	Party at Pete and Jenny's
Sunday	Visit parents in Oxford

2 Write sentences about her plans for the week ahead.

____
____
____
____
____

3 Complete the agenda for your week.

Monday	
Tuesday	
Wednesday	
Thursday	
Friday	
Saturday	
Sunday	

4 Write sentences about your plans.

____
____
____
____
____

25 Eating out

VOCABULARY

1 Complete the sentences with words from the list.

menu taste waiter tip bill course coffee reservation starter order dessert service

a When you arrive at the restaurant a __________ shows you where to sit.
b The waiter brings you the __________ at the end of the meal.
c There is often a __________ charge but some people leave a __________ as well.
d The first course or __________ is usually something light, a salad, for example.
e After the dessert you can have a __________.
f Before you go to the restaurant, it is a good idea to make a __________.
g He brings you the __________ and leaves you to choose.
h This is followed by the main __________ and finally the __________.
i If you have wine he asks you to __________ it.
j He comes and takes your __________.

2 The sentences describe what happens in a restaurant. Put them in the right order.

READING AND LISTENING

1 Look at the dialogues. What are the situations?

a in a restaurant
b in a pub
c a school canteen
d at home

Dialogue 1

A Look, there are some seats in the corner.
B You three go and sit down and I'll get the orders. What would you like?
A I'd like a gin and tonic, please.
B Would you like ice with your gin?
A Yes, please.
C And I'd like a mineral water, please. No ice.
B Would you like anything to eat?
A No, thanks.
C I'd like some crisps, please.

Dialogue 2

A Would you like some salad with your steak?
B No, thanks, but can I have some more chips, please.
A Yes, help yourself. But leave some for your sister.
B Can I get the tomato ketchup?
A Yes, it's in the fridge. Can you bring me a glass of water from the kitchen?
B Is there any mustard?
A I'm afraid there isn't any left.

2 Listen to the dialogues and underline anything that is different.

3 Listen again and correct the dialogues above. Write the corrections above the words and phrases you underlined.

FUNCTIONS

1 Who would say these sentences in a restaurant? The waiter or the customer?

1 Can I help you?
2 I'd like to order now, please.
3 What would you like to start with?
4 Would you like anything to drink?
5 Can you bring me the wine list, please?
6 What flavour would you like?
7 I'd like an ice cream, please.
8 Can I pay with a credit card?

2 Write suitable responses to the sentences in activity 1.

1 *We'd like a table for two, please.*
2 ______
3 ______
4 ______
5 ______
6 ______
7 ______
8 ______

3 Write suitable questions.

1 ______
Yes, I'd like cheesecake, please.
2 ______
I'm sorry, we're out of chips.
3 ______
Chocolate, please.
4 ______
I'd like pizza, please.
5 ______
Certainly, madam.
6 ______
Yes, I do. It's very good.

SOUNDS

Listen to these questions. Does the speaker sound polite and friendly?

1 Can you bring me some water, please?
2 Can I come with you?
3 I'd like an ice cream, please.
4 Can you take me to the station?
5 Can I have a German beer, please?
6 Can you turn the TV off, please?

Listen again and repeat. Try to sound polite and friendly.

WRITING

1 Write a short dialogue in a restaurant. Use the sentences in *Functions* activity 1.

______

2 Write a paragraph describing the last time you went to a restaurant.

______

26 Can I help you?

GRAMMAR

1 Complete the words to make reflexive pronouns.

my *self* your____ him____
her____ it____
our____ your____ them____

2 Complete the sentences with a reflexive pronoun.

1 I often buy flowers for ____________.
2 They are building the house ____________.
3 He does all the cooking ____________.
4 You can do it ____________!
5 We enjoyed ____________ last night.

3 Write sentences with a reflexive pronoun.

He wanted some Belgian chocolates. (buy)
He bought himself some Belgian chocolates.

1 They went to a good party and had a good evening. (enjoy)
____
2 She wants to speak French. She has a self-study book. (teach)
____
3 He has nobody to talk to. (talk)
____

VOCABULARY

1 Match the words on the left with a word on the right to make new words.

brief	glasses	*briefcase*
news	coat	
tooth	burger	
sun	paper	
hand	case	
rain	paste	
ham	bag	

2 Where can you buy the items in activity 1? Write sentences.

1 *You can buy a briefcase in a department store.*
2 ____________________________________
3 ____________________________________
4 ____________________________________
5 ____________________________________
6 ____________________________________
7 ____________________________________

3 Correct these expressions.

1 a box of shampoo ____________
2 a tube of biscuits ____________
3 a can of matches ____________
4 a bar of toothpaste ____________
5 a bottle of chocolate ____________
6 a packet of tomatoes ____________

4 Write down more products you find in the containers in activity 3.

____
____
____
____
____
____
____

SOUNDS

1 Listen to the words in *Vocabulary* activity 1 and underline the stressed syllables. What is the rule for these words?

2 Listen to these sentences and underline the stressed words.

1 It's too big.
2 I don't like it.
3 It doesn't suit me.
4 It doesn't fit me.
5 I don't like the colour.

Say the sentences aloud.

LISTENING AND FUNCTIONS

1 Listen to the dialogue and say what the situation is.

____

2 Are these sentences true or false?

1 The customer wants to buy a raincoat.
2 He likes a dark blue coat.
3 It doesn't fit him.
4 It's too small.
5 There's isn't a blue coat in his size.
6 He doesn't like green because it doesn't suit him.
7 He doesn't buy the black coat because it is too big.

3 Correct the false sentences in activity 2.

____
____
____

4 What expressions does the customer use to say that:

1 he wants to buy the black coat?

____

2 he doesn't want to buy it?

____

WRITING

Write two short dialogues between a shop assistant and a customer. Choose from these items:

sunglasses   an item of jewellery   a swimsuit
a watch

____
____
____
____
____
____
____
____
____

27 Whose bag is this?

VOCABULARY

1 What materials are these objects usually made of?

binoculars ______

a wallet ______

an umbrella ______

a book ______

2 Complete the crossword.

Across
1 You can see very far with them.
3 It keeps you dry in the rain.
5 The Lost _____ Office is where you go if you lose something.
8 Tables and chairs are often made of this material.
10 It's Peter's.
11 Silver or gold, for example.

Down
1 You put things in it.
2 It takes photos.
4 Not old.
6 You keep money in it.
7 Not thin.
9 Opposite of *in*.

SOUNDS

1 Listen to some words with the same-sounding ending.

calculator camera computer leather paper rectangular umbrella

Now say the words aloud.

2 Listen and underline the stressed words in the questions and answers.

1 Are they your letters? No, they're his.
2 Is this your bag? No, it's hers.
3 Is this her umbrella? No, it's mine.
4 Is this their car? No, it's ours.
5 Is this your book? No, it's yours.
6 Is this our table? No, it's theirs.

Listen again and say the answers aloud.

GRAMMAR

1 Write suitable questions.

1 ______
It's round.

2 ______
It's black.

3 ______
It's made of leather.

4 ______
No, that isn't mine.

5 ______
They're Janet's books.

6 ______
There's a purse, a box of matches and an address book in it.

2 Rewrite the sentences with a possessive pronoun.

1 It's my property. *It's mine.* ____________
2 It's his car. ____________
3 It's their house. ____________
4 They're our binoculars. ____________
5 They're her suitcases. ____________
6 It's your purse. ____________

READING AND WRITING

1 What question do the passages below answer?

1 Where do you keep valuable objects?
2 How do you remember where things are?
3 What do you lose?

2 Underline the things the writers often lose. Who is the most careful?

3 Are you like any of the writers? What do you lose regularly?

4 Write a similar paragraph in answer to the question.

____
____
____
____
____
____
____
____
____
____

A I lose things every day, but never very important things. I always find them again. The trouble is, when I find them it's too late. I don't need them anymore! It really is annoying. For example, I need to post a letter so I look for the stamps I bought yesterday. Of course, I can't find them so I buy some more. Every morning I spend at least ten minutes looking for my purse. I get really angry because it's always in a stupid place.

B I am usually very careful with my things. However, there are some things which I just can't keep. Umbrellas, for example. I buy two or three umbrellas every year. I put them down in shops, restaurants or in the cinema and I forget them. When I go back to get them, they're never there. Now I always buy very cheap umbrellas!

C I lose papers and keys – usually important papers. I also regularly leave my phone card in the telephone, and my cash card in the cashpoint machine. Last month I left my bag at the supermarket. Luckily, they phoned me and I went back to get it. Another thing I often lose is my car keys. Last week I lost them so I took the bus to work. When I got home I found them in the rubbish bin!

D I'm usually very good. I don't often lose anything. Once I left my overcoat in a restaurant but I went back the next day and they gave it to me. I never lose papers because I put them in my filing cabinet immediately. I always leave my car keys in the car so I can't lose them. I never lock the door of the house so I don't need a key and therefore I can't lose it!

28 What's the matter?

VOCABULARY

1 Write down twelve or more parts of the body.

____

____

____

2 What's the matter? Match the people in the pictures with the complaints.

a He's got a high temperature.
b She's got a cold.
c He's got a headache.
d She's got a sore finger.
e He's got toothache.

3 What's the matter? Write five possible answers with the verbs below.

hurt feel have got

1 throat ______________________________
2 back ______________________________
3 faint ______________________________
4 dizzy ______________________________
5 cough ______________________________

GRAMMAR AND FUNCTIONS

1 Give advice to the people in *Vocabulary* activity 2.

1 *You should* ______________________________
2 ______________________________
3 ______________________________
4 ______________________________
5 ______________________________

2 Say what the people *shouldn't* do.

1 *He shouldn't* ______________________________
2 ______________________________
3 ______________________________
4 ______________________________
5 ______________________________

3 Complete the dialogue with the sentences below.

MAN (1) ______________________________
WOMAN No, I don't feel very well.
MAN (2) ______________________________
WOMAN I feel sick.
MAN (3) ______________________________
WOMAN And I've got a headache.
MAN (4) ______________________________
WOMAN I think so. I feel very hot.

a What's the matter?
b Have you got a temperature?
c Oh dear!
d Are you all right?

Listen and check.

4 Write advice for the person in activity 3.

____

____

____

____

____

____

SOUNDS

1 Listen and repeat these questions.

1 Are you all right?
2 What's the matter?
3 Have you got a temperature?
4 Do you feel ill?
5 Does your back hurt?
6 What did the doctor say?

2 How many syllables are there in these words? Listen and put them into the correct list. Underline the stressed syllables.

accident aspirin complaint exercise hospital medicine private treatment temperature

Two syllables ______________________

____

Three syllables ______________________

____

Say the words aloud.

READING AND WRITING

1 Look at the passage about holiday health. What are the two paragraphs about?

insects water safety sun health insurance stomach problems

2 Read the passage and find these words. Check that you understand their meaning.

sunstroke shade symptoms mosquitoes malaria

3 Read the passage and underline advice with *should* or *shouldn't*.

4 Write four sentences of advice with *should* or *shouldn't*.

____

____

____

____

5 Write advice for the extra topics in activity 1.

____

____

____

____

Holiday health

A Many people travel to foreign countries to find the sun. So sunburn and sunstroke are common holiday complaints. You shouldn't stay in the sun too long. In very hot countries, you should stay out of the sun at midday for at least two hours. It is a good idea to sit in the shade if you can and wear a hat. If you lie in the sun you should use suncream. And remember, you can burn under water! If you stay in the sun too long without a hat, you can get sunstroke which can be quite serious. You have a high temperature and a headache. If you get these symptoms, you should lie down in a cool place, drink a lot of water and take an aspirin. If your temperature stays high, you should call a doctor.

B In some countries, insects, especially mosquitoes, are a health danger. You can wear long trousers and shirt sleeves to protect your arms and legs. You can also buy special cream to keep mosquitoes away from your body. At night, it's not a good idea to leave windows open when there are lights. In some countries, mosquitoes are dangerous because they carry malaria. When you go to these countries you should take medicine every day.

29 Country factfile

VOCABULARY AND SOUNDS

1 Find 22 adjectives in the puzzle. They go (→) and (↓). Some letters may be used more than once.

H	L	O	N	G	O	O	D	Y
E	O	L	I	G	H	T	S	O
A	W	D	R	Y	B	I	G	U
V	E	I	S	H	I	G	H	N
Y	T	R	A	S	L	O	W	G
H	O	T	F	A	S	T	D	C
B	S	Y	E	A	S	Y	A	O
A	D	S	M	A	L	L	R	L
D	M	O	D	E	R	N	K	D

2 Complete the chart with the comparative and superlative forms of the adjectives.

	Comparative	Superlative
good	______	______
bad	______	______
heavy	______	______
old	______	______
low	______	______
easy	______	______
big	______	______
wet	______	______

3 Write the complete forms for these abbreviations.

1 °C *degrees Centigrade*
2 m ______
3 mm ______
4 kph ______
5 km ______
6 sq km ______
7 kg ______
8 l ______

4 Complete the sentences with the correct abbreviations.

1 The average temperature in Thailand in January is 25______.
2 The highest point in Great Britain is 1,343______.
3 The average annual rainfall in the UK is 600______.
4 The UK covers a land area of 242,429______.
5 The maximum speed on motorways in France is 130______.
6 New York City's coastline is 920______ long.
7 One litre of water weighs 1______.

Listen and check.

5 Listen and repeat these measurements.

16°C 25 sq km 150 kph 2 kg 18°C 5,749 m
250 km 760 mm 36,790 sq km 57 kg

READING AND GRAMMAR

1 Read the passage about Brazil and match the headings with the paragraphs.

1 Population
2 Land area
3 Climate
4 Cities
5 Rivers

2 Underline the comparative and superlative phrases.

3 Correct these statements.

1 Brazil is bigger than Canada.

______

2 Brazil has a smaller population than Chile.

______

3 The Nile is wider than the Amazon.

______

4 Rio is bigger than São Paulo.

______

5 Most Brazilians live in the country areas.

______

4 Make comparisons.

1 Brazil and Argentina

2 The Amazon and the Nile

3 Brazil and Peru

4 Rio and São Paulo

5 June and December

A Brazil is the world's fourth largest country after Canada, China and the USA. It borders every country in South America except Chile and Ecuador. Its surface area is 8½ million sq km. It covers almost half of the South American continent.

B The world's second longest river is the Amazon. It is 6,300 km long. It crosses Brazil and carries 20% of the world's fresh water. It is the world's widest river and it covers the largest area.

C Brazil's population is around 140 million. It is the country with the highest population in South America and the 6th highest in the world. It is not very densely populated, with an average of only 15 people per sq km. Most of the population is concentrated along the coast and in the cities.

D Three out of four Brazilians now live in cities. São Paulo is South America's biggest city. It has over 15 million people. Rio de Janeiro, with over 10 million people is smaller than São Paulo but it is more densely populated.

E The Brazilian winter is from June to August, but it is only cold south of Rio, where the average temperature during the winter months is between 13°C and 18°C. The warmest months are from December to February. The Amazon basin receives the most rainfall, but it is not very hot – the average temperature is 27°C; but it is humid.

5 Rewrite the sentences using *as ... as*.

Canada is larger than the USA.
The USA is not as large as Canada.

1 São Paulo is bigger than Rio.

2 Rio is warmer than São Paulo.

3 The climate on the coast is drier than the climate in the Amazon basin.

4 The Nile is longer than the Amazon.

5 It is warmer in December than it is in June.

6 Write five sentences comparing your country to other places.

1 clean

2 wet

3 safe

4 hot

5 small

WRITING

Write a short description of your country.

30 Olympic spirit

VOCABULARY

1 Match words on the left with words on the right to form the name of a sport.

hang	surfing
motor	riding
wind	ball
horse	racing
basket	gliding

2 Write down words you associate with the sports in activity 1. You can look in your Student's Book.

1 ____________________
2 ____________________
3 ____________________
4 ____________________
5 ____________________

3 Choose an adjective to describe your opinion of each of the sports in activity 1.

dangerous exciting boring fast difficult expensive fashionable tiring interesting enjoyable popular safer

____
____
____
____
____

GRAMMAR

1 Complete the sentences with *more* or *most*.

1 Horse riding is the ________ expensive sport.
2 Baseball is ________ popular in the US than in Britain.
3 The ________ popular sport in France is cycling.
4 Hang gliding is one of the ________ dangerous sports in the world.
5 Motor racing is ________ exciting than horse racing.
6 Tennis is ________ fashionable than football.

2 Write sentences comparing the sports in *Vocabulary* activity 1.

Basketball is more popular than hang gliding.

1 ____________________
2 ____________________
3 ____________________
4 ____________________
5 ____________________

3 Write sentences using the superlative about the sports in *Vocabulary* activity 1.

Basketball is one of the most popular sports in the world.

1 ____________________
2 ____________________
3 ____________________
4 ____________________
5 ____________________

4 Do you agree? If not, give your opinion.

1 Formula 1 motor racing is the most exciting sport in the world.

____

2 Golf is the most difficult game to understand.

____

3 Baseball is the most interesting sport I know.

____

4 The most dangerous sport is horse riding.

____

5 Skiing is not as fashionable as tennis.

____

READING AND WRITING

1 Read the passage. Which sentence best describes the main idea?

1 It's important to travel to foreign countries.
2 Foreign places often seem more interesting than home.
3 Home is the best place to be.

2 Underline all the comparatives of long adjectives.

3 Write similar sentences for the words in the last section of the passage. Here are some adjectives you can use.

light tasty strange long exciting efficient friendly colourful polite

Breakfasts are lighter.

____

- The weather is better.
- The food is better – in particular, the fish is fishier, and the soups soupier.
- The light is brighter.
- The snow is whiter.
- The people are more polite and seem happier.
- The wine is cheaper.
- The buildings are more beautiful.
- The sea is warmer.
- The bars keep more civilised hours.
- The men are more good-looking and the women more sophisticated.
- The street life is livelier.
- Cakes and gateaux are more mouthwatering.
- The smells are more exotic.
- The sounds are more exciting.
- The markets are more interesting and their cheeses cheesier.
- The language is more expressive.
- The monuments are more monumental.
- The scenery is more spectacular, with the hills and mountains higher and the flat bits flatter.
- And so many ordinary things are different – breakfast, street signs, shops, clothes, children, the ringing of telephones, matches, bread, shop assistants, bank clerks – that nothing is ordinary at all.

4 Write sentences to describe your first impressions when you went to another country. Which of the ideas in the passage do you agree with?

____

When in Rome, do as the Romans do

GRAMMAR

1 How old must you be in your country to do these things?

get married
You must be sixteen years old.

1 drive a car
______

2 drive a motorbike
______

3 go into a bar without an adult
______

4 vote
______

5 buy cigarettes
______

6 leave school
______

2 Match the rules with the situations.

1 You mustn't smoke or use a computer during take off and landing. ☐
2 You mustn't give food to the animals. ☐
3 You mustn't leave your bags unattended. ☐
4 You must have a shower before you go in. ☐
5 You must keep dogs on a lead. ☐
6 You must wear a seat belt. ☐
7 You mustn't talk. ☐
8 You mustn't use your hands. ☐

a in an exam
b in a park
c in a car
d at a zoo
e during a football match
f at an airport
g at a swimming pool
h in a plane

3 Complete the sentences with *must* or *mustn't*.

1 You ______ make a noise in a library.
2 You ______ walk on the grass.
3 You ______ have a visa to enter some countries.
4 You ______ go into a pub without an adult.
5 You ______ smoke in the classroom.
6 You ______ take your shoes off when you go into a mosque.
7 You ______ always carry your identity card in some countries.
8 You ______ take a mobile phone into exams.

4 Are the sentences in activity 3 rules or strong advice?

5 Write one more rule for each of the situations in activity 2.

1 ______
2 ______
3 ______
4 ______
5 ______
6 ______
7 ______
8 ______

READING

1 Look at the notices and match them with the places.

1 Town park
2 Golf club
3 Public library
4 Swimming pool

2 Read Notice A. Match the information in the notice with the pictures.

A *You are not allowed to climb the trees.*

B ____________________

C ____________________

D ____________________

E ____________________

F ____________________

A

Opening hours:
8 am to 8 pm from 1st October to 30th April
10 am to 10 pm from 1st May to 30th September
RULES:
put litter in bins
no golf
no cycling
keep your dog on a lead
You are not allowed to:
– sleep overnight on the benches
– stay inside after closing time
– walk on the flower beds
– climb the trees

3 Read Notice B and underline two sentences with *must* or *mustn't*.

4 Write more sentences for both notices saying what people must or mustn't do.

Notice A

You mustn't play golf in the park.

Notice B

You mustn't wear shorts.

WRITING

Write a list of rules for the two extra places in *Reading* activity 1.

____
____
____
____
____
____
____
____
____
____

B

Opening hours:
10 am to 7.30 pm on weekdays
9 am to 9.30 pm at weekends
Rules:
– you must wear proper swimsuits
– shorts are not allowed
– an adult must stay with children under six at all times
– no running or jumping
– no smoking in the pool area
– food and drink are not allowed near the pool

32 Have you ever been to London?

READING

1 Read the passage and list the jobs that Jane has had.

a model

____

____

2 Underline the sentences in the present perfect.

3 Circle three sentences in the simple past.

Jobs are my career

Jane Brooks has had fifty-four jobs in four years and still hasn't found her ideal career. She has been a model, a waitress, an actress, a nanny and a ticket seller. The shortest job she had was as a cook in a canteen. She left it after just two hours. The longest job she had was as a zoo-keeper. She stayed in that job for two months.

Jane, 23, of Southampton, is now working in telesales. She says, 'I just haven't found a career I really enjoy. I'll keep trying different jobs until I do.'

GRAMMAR

1 Put the words into two groups. Some words can go in both groups.

ate been drunk had driven read left saw flown wore taken bought made went written sold fought met found took eaten flew drove gone wrote seen worn

Past participle ______________________________

____

Past simple ______________________________

____

2 Put the words in order and write sentences.

1 a you been ever country to have foreign?

____

2 has he on never television appeared.

____

3 visited I a lot have countries of.

____

4 Spain went last they year to.

____

5 did Spain when go they to?

____

3 Complete the questions with a suitable past participle from the list in activity 1. Answer the questions with a *yes* or *no* answer.

Have you ever *been* to a football match?

Yes, I have.

1 Have you ever __________ champagne?

____

2 Have you ever __________ a Mercedes?

____

3 Have you ever __________ a film star?

____

4 Have you ever __________ a hat?

____

5 Have you ever __________ in a plane?

____

6 Have you ever __________ traditional English food?

____

7 Have you ever __________ a book?

____

8 Have you ever __________ an exam?

____

4 Choose the correct verb form.

1 I *have never been/never went* to Japan.
2 We *went/have gone* to stay with my aunt last year.
3 He *has found/find* an interesting job at last.
4 I *have met/met* her last week.
5 She *has never flown/never flew* in a plane before.
6 She *has drunk/drank* champagne on her birthday.

5 Complete the dialogues with *gone, been* or *went.*

1 A Have you ever __________ to Russia?
B Yes, I have. I __________ there last summer.
2 A Where's Peter __________? I've phoned him three times this week and he's not at home.
B He's __________ to Brussels on business. I think he __________ on Monday. He'll be back at the weekend.

LISTENING

1 Write down things or places you associate with these countries.

Russia ______________________________
Australia ______________________________
Switzerland ______________________________
Mexico ______________________________
Japan ______________________________

2 Listen to a conversation. Which countries have they visited?

Man ______________________________
Woman ______________________________

3 Listen again and tick the things they have seen or the places they have visited.

kangaroos ☐
Lake Constance ☐
mountain scenery ☐
Sydney Opera House ☐
the Kremlin ☐
Moscow ☐
surfing beaches ☐
Red Square ☐
Zürich ☐
a ski resort ☐

4 Write four sentences saying what they have seen or visited.

____
____
____
____
____
____
____
____

WRITING

1 Look back at the passage in *Reading* and write a similar paragraph describing your job experience.

____
____
____
____
____
____
____

2 Listen to the conversation in *Listening* again and write a few lines describing your travel experience. Say where you have been, what you have seen and what you haven't seen in these places.

____
____
____
____
____
____
____
____
____
____

33 What's happened?

SOUNDS

1 Listen and repeat these questions. Notice the intonation.

1 Have you seen the doctor yet?
2 Have you ever met her?
3 Have they done the shopping yet?
4 Has he been here before?
5 Has she bought her ticket?

2 Listen and repeat these words.

break crashed drilled dropped crossed parked scored

3 How do you pronounce the *a* in these words? Put the words into three groups.

age back park bag car crash exam face pay plate sharp stay take

/eɪ/ *age* ________________
/æ/ *back* ________________
/ɑː/ *park* ________________

Listen and check. Say the words aloud.

GRAMMAR AND VOCABULARY

1 Write the past participles of these irregular verbs.

steal ________
fall ________
leave ________
come ________
keep ________
break ________
run ________
catch ________
hurt ________
pay ________
lose ________
find ________

2 Complete the sentences with a verb in the present perfect. Choose from the list in activity 1.

1 He's at the police station because someone ________ his car.
2 She isn't playing tennis because she ________ a bad cold.
3 They ________ their cat and they're looking everywhere for it.
4 Why's he crying? Because he ________ off his bicycle.
5 Look, I ________ someone's wallet on the ground.
6 I'm afraid, I ________ the glass. I dropped it.

3 Put a tick (✓) if you use the present perfect and a cross (✗) if you use the past simple. Complete the example with the correct tense.

a to talk about experiences ☐
I ________ (never, visit) South America.

b to talk about a definite time in the past ☐
I ________ (visit) Spain last summer.

c to talk about an action which happened at an indefinite time in the past ☐
I ________ (read) that book. It's very good.

d for a recent action with *just* ☐
I ________ (just, had) a big meal.

e in questions with *yet* ☐
________ (do) your homework yet?

f for a past action which has a result in the present ☐
I'm taking him to the doctor's because he ________ (hurt) his leg.

g in questions with *when* ☐
When ________ (go) to Spain?

h to describe a series of actions in the past ☐
First we ________ (visit) the museum then we ________ (have) lunch.

LISTENING

1 Listen to a conversation. Tick (✓) the activities they talk about.

skiing	☐	dancing	☐
driving	☐	swimming	☐
cooking	☐	speaking English	☐
singing	☐	speaking in public	☐

2 Listen again and complete the sentences.

1 She can swim quite ________ but she can't swim very ________.
2 She's quite a ________ dancer.
3 She cooks very ________.
4 She drives too ________ in town and too ________ on the motorway.
5 She's a ________ driver.

3 Look at the list in activity 1. How well do you do each of these things? Write a sentence for each one.

____

____

____

____

____

____

READING

1 Read this passage about Italy. The writer is comparing northern and southern Italy. Which part of Italy does he prefer?

2 Underline all the adverbs in the passage. Check that you understand their meaning. You can use your dictionary.

3 Write down four things that people do in northern Italy.

They wear expensive designer clothes.

____

____

____

____

4 Write down four things people do in southern Italy.

They sit for hours in cafes.

____

____

____

____

After southern Italy, Milan didn't seem Italian at all. People walked quickly and purposefully, wearing expensive designer clothes. They didn't sit for hours in cafés drinking espressos and eating mountains of pasta. They didn't argue passionately about unimportant things. They took life seriously. They had meetings. They did business. They talked on car phones. They drove slowly, mostly in BMWs and Porsches and they parked carefully. The women all looked like *Vogue* models. It was like a town of southern California in Italy. But this was Italy. And I wanted the noisy street life, washing hanging across the streets, people shouting noisily, scooters honking their horns ...

WRITING

Look back at the *Reading* passage. Write a similar description of people in a town you have visited.

____

____

____

____

____

____

____

____

36 I'll go by train

VOCABULARY AND READING

1 Match words in Box A with words in Box B to form new words or expressions.

A	B
passport first check departure petrol baggage ticket arrival boarding	reclaim office station class hall lounge control pass in

____

____

____

____

____

2 These sentences describe what you do when you travel by plane. Put them in order.

a You show your boarding pass to the steward and you board the plane.

b You go through passport control, through customs and into the arrival hall.

c It's usual to book your flight.

d The plane lands.

e You leave your luggage at the check-in and they give you a boarding pass.

f You wait in the departure lounge until they call your flight, and then go to the right gate.

g The plane takes off.

h It's important to go to the right terminal if you want to be on time.

i You go through passport control.

3 What means of transport are the sentences below about?

Train ______________________

Plane ______________________

Car ______________________

Boat ______________________

1 I love travelling but I hate aircraft, airports, air terminals and everything to do with them.

2 It's often expensive to have a full meal on a train and the food is often bad.

3 I'd like to travel everywhere by rail because it's so relaxing.

4 It is more and more difficult to get a drink on a short flight.

5 To drive in many countries you need to get an international licence.

6 I love arriving in a city by river. For example, it's wonderful to go down the Danube to Budapest.

7 You should buy a good road map before you start your journey.

8 It is still possible to travel by rail in comfort.

9 It's a good idea to stop for a rest every two hours when you are on a long journey.

10 When the sea is rough it can be very uncomfortable.

4 Put a tick (✓) by the sentences in activity 3 which say positive things and a cross (x) by those which say negative things about the means of transport.

5 Write positive and negative things about travelling on a bicycle.

____

____

____

____

____

____

SOUNDS

Listen and put a tick (✓) by the sentence you hear.

1 a I won't take the train.
  b I want to take the train.
2 a I'll buy a return ticket.
  b I buy a return ticket.
3 a We'll stay here tonight.
  b Will you stay here tonight?
4 a You'll like this restaurant.
  b You like this restaurant.
5 a I'll check my flight.
  b I check my flight.

Listen again and check.

GRAMMAR AND LISTENING

1 Put the words in order and write the questions.

1 he go will sightseeing when?

______

2 you single have a will room?

______

3 will long in how you stay London?

______

4 the you will get from hotel the airport to how?

______

5 evening will have where you dinner this?

______

2 Match these answers with the questions in activity 1.

a For a week. d At the weekend.
b By taxi. e No, a double.
c At home.

3 Write down five things you will do this week if you have time.

I'll wash the car.

1 ______
2 ______
3 ______
4 ______
5 ______

4 Listen to a conversation. What is the situation?

a Choosing an evening's television
b Sightseeing
c Planning an evening out

5 Listen again and correct these sentences.

1 She'll stay in bed until 10 o'clock.

______

2 She won't have breakfast.

______

3 She'll visit the Louvre in the afternoon.

______

4 She'll have lunch at the hotel.

______

5 She'll go up the Eiffel Tower in the morning.

______

6 Write down four other things she will do. Use these words.

Notre Dame Cathedral Montmartre district
shopping for souvenirs glass of wine

1 ______
2 ______
3 ______
4 ______

WRITING

Imagine you are taking a visitor sightseeing in your town or country. Write sentences about where you will go and what you will do.

______

37 What will it be like in the future?

VOCABULARY

1 Write the adjectives from these nouns. You can use your dictionary.

sun	________	cloud	________
rain	________	fog	________
cold	________	heat	________
wind	________	warmth	________
snow	________	wet	________

2 Match items 1 to 6 below with the weather symbols A to F.

A

B

C

D

E

F

1 Sunshine	4 Thunderstorm
2 Temperature	5 Rain
3 Snow	6 Wind speed and direction

3 What is the best weather for these activities?

having a picnic ________________

sailing ________________

a seaside holiday ________________

growing tomatoes ________________

working indoors ________________

SOUNDS

Listen and circle the temperatures you hear.

11°C -8°C 27°C 0°C -1°C 16°C 19°C -3°C
35°C 7°C -4°C 13°C 24°C -10°C

Say them aloud.

GRAMMAR

1 Look at tomorrow's weather map. What will the weather be like in the following places?

1 Venice ________________

2 Naples ________________

3 Milan ________________

4 Sicily ________________

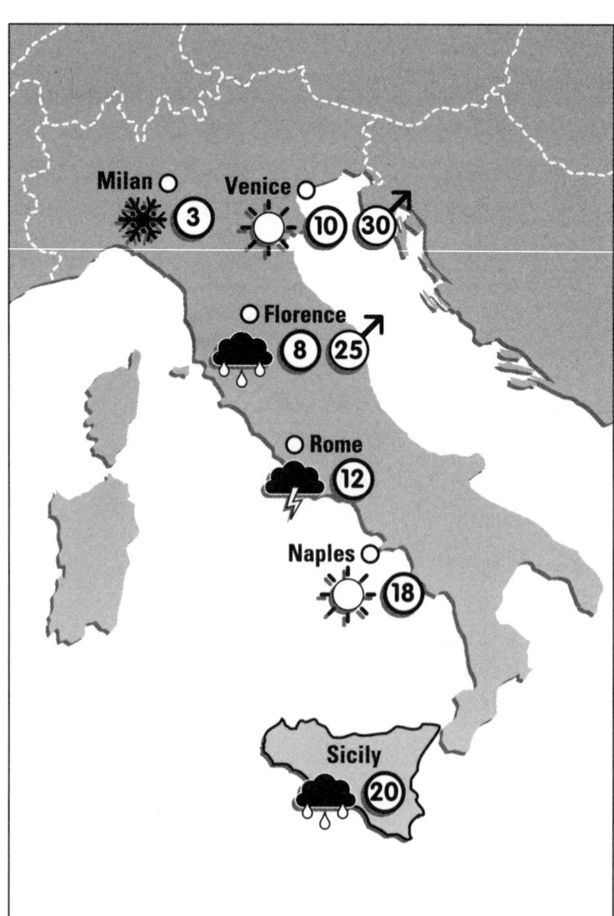

2 Write about the weather in the places in activity 1 using *won't*.

It won't be sunny and warm. It won't be a nice day.

1 ______
2 ______
3 ______
4 ______

3 What is the weather like today where you are? What will it be like in the next few days? Write a few sentences.

______

4 Complete the sentences with a verb in the future.

1 In the future the world ______ warmer.
2 Many cities ______ underwater.
3 In Britain snow at Christmas ______ very rare.
4 Crops ______ more quickly in the hotter climate.
5 Temperatures ______ by 2–6°C.
6 Ice at the North Pole ______.

READING AND LISTENING

1 Read the predictions for the future. Put *O* by the optimistic predictions and *P* by the pessimistic predictions.

1 There will be too many people in the world.
2 Most people will live more healthy lives.
3 There won't be enough food for everyone.
4 The world economy will get better.
5 Farmers will produce more crops.
6 There won't be enough petrol.
7 Fresh water will be very expensive.
8 Many big cities will disappear underwater.
9 People will live longer and happier lives.
10 There will be fewer species of wild animals.

2 Listen to a conversation. Who is optimistic for the future? Who is pessimistic?

3 Listen again and put a tick (✓) by the predictions in activity 1 which they make.

4 Are you optimistic or pessimistic about the future? Which predictions do you agree with?

______

WRITING

1 Write some predictions about the future of the world.

______

2 Write predictions about your life next year.

I'll be able to speak English quite well.

______

38 Hamlet was written by Shakespeare

SOUNDS

1 Look at the example and correct the sentences.

1 Tea is grown in Brazil. (India)
No, it isn't. It's grown in India.

2 The telephone was invented by Marconi. (Bell)
____

3 *Guernica* was painted by Monet. (Picasso)
____

4 *Hamlet* was written by Spencer. (Shakespeare)
____

5 Toyota cars are made in the United States. (Japan)
____

6 The Pyramids were built by Alexander the Great. (The Pharaohs)
____

Listen and check your answers.

2 Underline the stressed syllables in these words.

pottery computer tobacco coffee compose invent discover Japanese consume appreciate introduce

Listen and check your answers.

VOCABULARY AND GRAMMAR

1 Put the words in the list by the verbs you would use them with.

rice house Halley's comet oranges Australia potatoes dynamite mosque telephone church Jupiter coffee penicillin the Pyramids cotton

invent ____________________
grow ____________________
discover ____________________
build ____________________

2 Complete these sentences with verbs from activity 1.

1 They __________ rice in Vietnam.
2 Sultan Ahmed __________ the Blue Mosque in Istanbul.
3 Fleming __________ penicillin in 1928.
4 The Spanish __________ oranges in the region of Valencia.
5 The Europeans __________ Australia in the 17th century.
6 The Chinese __________ gunpowder in the 9th century.

3 Put a tick (✓) by the sentences in activity 2 which are in the present tense and a cross (x) by those in the past tense.

4 Re-write the sentences in activity 2 in the passive.

1 *Rice is grown in Vietnam.*
2 ____________________
3 ____________________
4 ____________________
5 ____________________
6 ____________________

5 Write five more sentences in the passive with the verbs in activity 1.

1 ____________________
2 ____________________
3 ____________________
4 ____________________
5 ____________________

6 Write down the names of two:

famous paintings ____________________
songs or pieces of music ____________________
famous buildings ____________________
books you like ____________________

7 Write sentences in the passive with the names you wrote in activity 6.

The Mona Lisa was painted by Leonardo da Vinci.

____

____

____

____

____

____

____

READING AND WRITING

1 Write the past participles of these verbs. Check that you understand their meaning.

drink ______________
introduce ______________
appreciate ______________
grow ______________
sell ______________
dry ______________
enjoy ______________
consume ______________
heat ______________

2 Read passage A about tea and underline all the verbs in the passive. You can use a dictionary to help you with difficult vocabulary.

3 Read the next two passages. Can you guess what *it* is in each passage? Turn to page 91 and check your answers.

4 What are people's attitudes to these products in your country? When and how are they consumed? Write a few lines for each product.

____

____

____

____

____

____

A

Tea comes from a tree which is grown in countries where the climate is warm and quite wet. The leaves are dried and heated. It was first grown as a commercial crop in China in the 8th century. It was introduced into Europe in the 17th century. Today it is grown in India, China and Sri Lanka and it is sold to countries all over the world.

B

Half a billion cups of *it* are drunk in the world every day.
It was introduced to Europe in the 17th century and was for a long time enjoyed only by rich people. Today *it* is mostly grown in South America and eastern Africa.
It is now one of the most popular hot drinks in Europe. On average, in Scandinavia, 10.5 kg are drunk per person each year. Only 3.5 kg are drunk in southern Europe.
It is drunk at the start of each day and after each meal.
It is appreciated by workers because *it* helps them concentrate.
Many people don't drink *it* in the evening because *it* keeps them awake.
Nobody really knows if *it* is good or bad for your health but almost everybody drinks *it*.

C

It was first consumed by native people in Latin America.
It was introduced into Spain and Portugal in the 16th century.
In the 17th century *it* was grown in North America and *it* was sold all over the world.
Today, a large part of the world crop is still grown in North and South America.
It is well known that *it* is bad for your health, but many people all over the world continue to smoke *it*.
In many countries *it* cannot be consumed in public places. In restaurants and bars there are areas where *it* can be consumed. And it is forbidden to sell *it* to children.

39 She said it wasn't far

GRAMMAR

1 Write what the people actually said.

1 She said it was open all year.

2 He said it started at half past nine.

3 He said that dinner was served at seven.

4 They said they were late because of the traffic.

5 She said she didn't like the food.

6 She said she wasn't staying another night.

2 Underline the correct verb tense.

1 He said he *was/is* in Brighton.
2 'The last train *leaves/left* at 9.30 on Saturdays,' she said.
3 She said it *costs/cost* fifteen pounds a night.
4 They said they *were/are* taking the first flight.
5 The receptionist said that dinner *was/is* at 7 o'clock.
6 'Dinner *is/was* at 7 o'clock,' said the receptionist.
7 They said it *was/is* only three kilometres from the hotel.
8 He said he *finishes/finished* the language course this week.

3 Write the sentences in reported speech.

1 'It's not far from the town centre,' said John.

2 'I don't like opera,' she said.

3 'The bus arrives at 9 o'clock,' she said.

4 'We've got a double room,' said the manager.

5 'It costs thirty pounds a night,' he said.

6 'The train takes half an hour,' she said.

7 'We don't want a television in the room,' they said.

8 'We're early. It doesn't leave until six thirty,' he said.

VOCABULARY

Think about the situations below. Write down words and expressions you can use in these situations.

a informing of a flat to buy

b informing of a flight delay

c informing of arrangements to go to a concert

d changing a lunch appointment

LISTENING AND READING

1 Listen to four telephone conversations. Match the conversations with the situations in *Vocabulary*.

Phone call 1 __________
Phone call 2 __________
Phone call 3 __________
Phone call 4 __________

2 Listen again and take the messages.

Phone call 1 *John Griffiths called; has tickets; concert at Palace Hall 8.30*
Phone call 2 ______________________
Phone call 3 ______________________
Phone call 4 ______________________

3 Look at your notes in activity 2 and underline the mistakes in this message.

John Griffiths called. He said he had the tickets for you both. He said the concert was at the Palace Hall and it started at 8.00. He said he was taking the train because it was cheaper and it left at 7 o'clock. He said he was in the office all day if you wanted to phone him.

4 Correct the mistakes in the message for Phone call 1.

____

5 Messages 2 and 3 are mixed up. Can you separate them?

Maria phoned to say she had a dentist's appointment at 1.30 tomorrow. Mrs Croft phoned to say she was at Charles de Gaulle Airport in Paris and her flight was delayed. She said she could meet you for coffee at 11 in Ascari's. She said she didn't know when she would arrive in London. She said you didn't need to meet her because she would get a taxi home. She said that if you didn't phone back she would see you there tomorrow at 11. She also said she had got the books you needed for college. She said that the new office over there was fine and the new manager seemed competent. And they only cost £5 each.

WRITING

Read the message for Phone call 1 again and write the telephone conversation.

A Can I speak to Peter, please? This is John Griffiths.

B I'm sorry, he's out at the moment. Can I take a message?

A ______________________

B ______________________

40 Dear Jan... Love Ruth

READING

1 Read the letter and find the answers to these questions.

1 Who is writing?
2 Who is she writing to?
3 Where is she?
4 Why is she there?

2 Put these sentences in the correct places in the letter.

a I'd like to find a job at the seaside.
b Last Saturday we went sightseeing to London for the day.
c Luckily, they are Czech so we speak English together.
d It was my first trip on a boat and I was ill!

3 Find one example of each of the verb tenses.

Dear Anna,
I'm sorry I haven't written to you earlier but I have been very busy. As you know, I left home on 5th April and I travelled by train and ferry to Britain. The ferry journey wasn't very nice because there was a lot of wind. (1) I won't travel on one again!
The language school here in Hastings is very good and I'm enjoying the classes. We work every morning from nine to one o'clock. In the afternoon there are organised visits and group activities. (2) I saw all the places I've seen pictures of in my English books.
I'm staying with a family who are very kind to me. There are two other students from my course staying here, too. (3) In the evenings we go to a pub or a disco. I've met lots of other students of different nationalities.
The course finishes at the end of June. I don't know exactly what I'll do in the summer. I think I'll stay here in Britain for July. (4) It'll be easier then because I hope my English will be better than it is now!
Love from
Maria

GRAMMAR

1 Underline the verbs in these sentences. Write the name of the tense. You can look in your Student's Book.

1 Jan went to Mario's room.
____
2 I'm staying with the Hawkins family.
____
3 I'll come to see you in the summer.
____
4 They haven't met many foreigners.
____
5 I like dancing.
____

2 Match the two parts of the sentences.

1 I'll come with you this afternoon
2 The man came out of the pub
3 I haven't visited Westminster
4 I like sightseeing
5 She's sitting in the bar

a because I've never been to London.
b if I finish my homework this morning.
c when the weather is good.
d waiting for you.
e and walked across the road.

3 Underline the words which are both past simple and past participle.

won spoke bought said stepped went sold came sent told eaten drank got made arrived left lost stolen been took read saw flew written climbed gone hurt found

4 Present perfect or past simple? Choose the correct tense.

1 He _______________ Ruth at a disco last Saturday. (meet)
2 She _______________ from a holiday in Spain. (just, come back)
3 I _______________ my car key. Can you help me find it? (lose)
4 He _______________ an award for the film in 1968. (win)
5 _______________ you _______________ this book by Thomas Hardy? It's very good. (read)
6 They _______________ in Britain two weeks ago. (arrive)
7 I'm afraid, I _______________ the shopping yet. (not, do)
8 When _______________ they _______________ the disco? (leave)

5 Present simple or present continuous? Choose the correct tense.

1 I _______________ in a hotel this week. (stay)
2 She always _______________ the bus to work in the morning. (take)
3 They _______________ going out in the evening. (not, like)
4 She _______________ very well today. I don't think she'll win. (not, play)
5 Most people _______________ in the city centre. (work)
6 _______________ you _______________ to football matches? (go, often)

6 Put a tick (✓) by the sentences which are predictions.

1 It's only half past five. We won't be late.
2 It's raining outside. I'll get my umbrella.
3 It's very cloudy now. I'm sure it'll rain this evening.
4 Have you met my brother? I'll introduce you to him.
5 My car is at the garage so we'll get the bus to the station.
6 Are you going to the concert? You'll really enjoy it.

7 Write sentences about yourself with these time expressions.

1 at the moment
____
2 last Saturday
____
3 tomorrow
____
4 never
____
5 every evening
____

WRITING

Imagine you are on an English course in Britain. Write a letter to a friend. Talk about:

your feelings when you arrived
where you are living   the school
your progress in English   who you have met
what you have seen   where you have been
your feelings now   your plans for the future

____
____
____
____
____
____
____
____
____
____
____
____
____
____
____
____
____
____
____
____
____
____

Tapescripts

LLesson 1 Sounds, activity 1

Japan China Canada Korea Germany
Russia Brazil Turkey Ukraine Morocco

Lesson 1 Listening, activity 1

Conversation 1

JUAN Hello, I'm Juan.
ANNA Hello, Juan. My name's Anna. I'm from France. Where are you from, Juan?
JUAN I'm from Barcelona in Spain.

Conversation 2

MR THOMAS Hello, my name's Thomas, Peter Thomas.
MR PLACIDI Hello, Mr Thomas. I'm Marco Placidi. I'm from Naples in Italy. Where are you from?
MR THOMAS I'm from Philadelphia in the United States of America.

Conversation 3

INGRID Hello, I'm Ingrid. What's your name?
SALLY Hello, Ingrid. My name's Sally. Where are you from?
INGRID I'm from Sweden. And you, Sally? Where are you from?
SALLY I'm from Toronto in Canada.

Conversation 4

JANET SMITH Hello, my name's Janet Smith.
MARILYN KELLY Hello, Mrs Smith. I'm Marilyn Kelly.
JANET SMITH Where are you from, Mrs Kelly?
MARILYN KELLY I'm from Sydney in Australia.

Lesson 2 Listening, activity 1

JAN Hi there. My name's Jan. I'm from America. I'm a secretary here at the university.
LEE Hello, Jan. My name's Lee. I'm from Buenos Aires in Argentina. I'm a teacher.
JAN This is my friend, Sara. She's from Canada. She's a student.
LEE Hello, Sara.
SARA Hello, Lee.

Lesson 2 Listening, activity 2

A Hello, Peter. What's your friend's name?
B His name's Silvio.
A Where's he from?
B He's from Italy.
A What's his job?
B He's an accountant.

Lesson 3 Sounds

1 Where are you from?
2 How old are you?
3 What is your address?
4 Who is your favourite actor?
5 Where is your home?
6 What is your telephone number?

Lesson 3 Listening, activity 1

INTERVIEWER Hello.
MARIA Hello.
INTERVIEWER I'm Sheila Grange. I'm the hotel manager. Please sit down. Now, what is your name?
MARIA My name is Maria Verde.
INTERVIEWER You are interested in a job here at the Continental Hotel. Is that right?
MARIA Yes, that's right.
INTERVIEWER What's your job now?
MARIA I'm a receptionist at the Hilton in London.
INTERVIEWER How old are you Miss Verde?
MARIA I'm twenty-five years old.
INTERVIEWER Are you married?
MARIA No, I'm single.
INTERVIEWER Are you British?
MARIA No, I'm Italian. I'm from Milan.
INTERVIEWER Your English is excellent!
MARIA Thank you.

Lesson 4 Grammar and Sounds, activity 1

43 13 97 56 51 12 63 17 8 94
77 15 85 3 39

Lesson 4 Grammar and Sounds, activity 2

classrooms teachers addresses numbers
colleges classes chairs

Lesson 5 Sounds, activity 1

1 WALLET 2 COLOUR 3 COMB
4 CAMERA 5 WATCH 6 DIARY

Lesson 5 Listening

A Where are my glasses ?
B What colour are they?
A Blue and green. They're not in my bag.
B Well, they're not on the table. Are they under your book?
A Oh, yes. Here they are. Thanks.

Lesson 6 Listening, activity 1

SPEAKER 1 We're a very big family. I'm very lucky, I suppose. I live alone now. My husband's dead. But my children have got houses near here. My daughter is a teacher here in the town and I see her at weekends. She's married. Her husband, Greg, is American. He's very nice and kind. He's got a job with a computer company. They've got a two-year-old daughter, Philippa. I've got three sons. Kevin and Josh are both married with children. Henry is still single. He's a medical student at university.
SPEAKER 2 I'm twenty-eight and I live in Britain now. I've got a good job here. My family are all in the States so I don't see them much. I'm married and we've got a beautiful daughter. Her name is Philippa. My wife, Sally, has got three brothers. Her father's dead and her mother lives near us. She's not very independent, though. Always at our home. She helps Sally look after our daughter. She's a wonderful grandmother and Philippa loves her.

Lesson 7 Sounds, activity 3

1 3.30 **2** 10.15 **3** 7.45 **4** 2.10 **5** 9. 55
6 1.35 **7** 11.30 **8** 7.00 **9** 4.05 **10** 6.40

Lesson 8 Listening, activity 1

SPEAKER 1 My favourite room is a small study where I work in the evenings. It's upstairs next to the bathroom at the back of the house so there is no noise from the road. There are bookcases on two walls of the room and a big desk in front of the window. My computer is on the desk. On one wall there's a big mirror and next to it there's an old armchair that I like very much. It's not a beautiful room but it's a very comfortable room.
SPEAKER 2 I live in a very big house with lots of rooms. The room I like best is a big sitting room at the back of the house. It is a pretty room with some beautiful old furniture. There's a big window with a beautiful view of the garden. There is a comfortable sofa in front of the fire where I sit in the evenings with my family. There are pretty green curtains in front of the window and an old piano next to it. The television and video are on a cupboard near the fire.
SPEAKER 3 My favourite room is my bedroom. It's upstairs at the front of the house. There's a view of the front garden and the town in the distance. In the room there's a bed and next to the bed there's a small table with a lamp. There's a big cupboard next to the door where I put my clothes. Near the window there's a big table with two chairs. There are some plants and a telephone on the table. It isn't really a beautiful room but it is not noisy and it's very comfortable.

Lesson 9 Listening, activity 1

WOMAN 1 I come home before my husband so I have a cup of tea. I listen to the radio and I make dinner. My husband comes home at about 7 and he watches the sport on TV. He doesn't like cooking. We eat in front of the TV. On Wednesdays I go to a friend's house for the evening. My husband goes to a club with friends or to the cinema.
On Saturday we go to town to the shops in the morning. My husband goes to a football match with friends in the afternoon and I go to a jazz club with my friends. In the evening we go to a restaurant or to a discotheque with friends. On Sundays we get up at midday, have lunch, and work in the house. My husband washes the car and I go running in the park. We watch TV and go to bed early.
WOMAN 2 I come home from work at about 6.30. I read the newspaper and relax. When my husband comes home, we have a drink together then he makes dinner. We eat in front of the television. On Tuesday evenings we go out with friends. We go to the cinema or to a nightclub. On Wednesdays I have a language class and

then I have dinner with a friend. I come home at 11.
On Saturdays we go to a supermarket to do the shopping for the week. And in the evening we go out with friends. Most Sundays we go to my parents' house for the afternoon. Some weekends we go to see friends in the country. In the evening I work on the computer.

Lesson 10 Listening, activity 1

Conversation 1

MAN I like this very much. What is it?
WOMAN I don't know. It's modern art. I don't like it at all.
MAN What about that painting near the door? It's very beautiful.
WOMAN No, it isn't. It's horrible! It's just a blue and red mess.
MAN Well, what do you like?
WOMAN I like classical paintings by real artists!
MAN I just like good paintings. Classical and modern.

Conversation 2

WOMAN Do you like the music?
MAN No. What is it?
WOMAN It's reggae. I love it. It's great for dancing. I come here every Saturday evening.
MAN It's very noisy.
WOMAN Do you like dancing?
MAN Well, um, I don't know. You see, this is my first visit to a night club.
WOMAN Well, what music do you like?
MAN I like classical music. I play the violin in an orchestra.
WOMAN I hate classical music. It's no good for dancing.

Lesson 11 Listening, activity 3

MUSICIAN I play in a club on Friday, Saturday and Wednesday evenings. I play the guitar in a rock group. There are four of us. On the nights we play I have a snack at home at 7 o'clock. I leave home at 8 o'clock and I take a taxi to the club. We usually start playing at 9.00 but I always get to the club at 8.15 to get things ready. We sometimes have a drink with the owner of the club. Most people arrive around 9.30. We usually play for an hour and a half, then we have a break. We always have a snack and a drink. We play again from 11.30 to about 1 o'clock. On Tuesday and Thursday mornings I practise with the other musicians.
CHEF I get up at 8.00 most mornings and have a shower and a big breakfast with my wife. My wife leaves for work at 8.45 and I relax and read the newspaper for half an hour. I leave the house at 9.40. The restaurant is near my home so I walk to work. I have lunch in the kitchen at 2 o'clock and then I walk home. My wife works in the mornings and she is usually at the house when I get home. In the afternoon I relax at home or go out to the park with my wife. At six o'clock I go back to work and I get home at 11 o'clock. I don't go to work on Sundays and Mondays.

Lesson 14 Listening, activity 1

Conversation 1

A Excuse me. Where can I get some stamps?
B At the post office.
A Is there a post office near here?
B Yes. Go along Broad Street. Turn right into the High Street, then straight ahead into High Town. The post office is opposite the book shop. Behind the Old House.
A Thank you very much.

Conversation 2

C Excuse me. Can you tell me where I can buy some aspirin?
D The best place is the chemist's in the High Street.
C Can you tell me where it is, please?
D Yes, of course. Walk along Broad Street. Turn right into the High Street. The chemist's is opposite the newsagent's. It's on the left of a sports shop.
C Thank you very much.

Conversation 3

E Hello, Peter. How are you?
F Fine thanks. Why are you here in town?
E I'm with my parents. We are looking for a nice place to eat. Can you tell me where there is a good Italian restaurant?
F Yes. There's a restaurant called Pasta in Widemarsh Street. It has a good reputation.
E How can I get to Widemarsh Street from here? Is it far?
F No. About five minutes' walk. Go down Broad Street. Turn right into the High Street, then turn left into Widemarsh Street. Go along there for about fifty metres and the restaurant is on the right opposite the baker's. There's a Chinese restaurant on the same side of the road.
E Thanks. Bye.

Lesson 15 Listening, activity 3

Conversation 1

A Bridgeton 319850.
B Hello. Is that you, mother? It's Anna.
A Hello Anna. Where are you phoning from?
B From the hotel. We're staying in a hotel right in the centre of the city. We can see the sea from our bedroom window.
A Are you enjoying yourselves?
B We're having a wonderful time. The city is very attractive and there are lots of interesting things to visit. The port is my favourite place. It's very exciting.
A Is the weather good?
B Not very good. It's raining at the moment. But it isn't cold.
A Well, have a good time, Anna. Phone me when you get home. Bye.
B Bye.

Conversation 2

C Penally 765 316.
D Hi, Jim. It's me, Stephie.
C Hello. How was your flight?
D Great! The plane was on time. No problems at all. Is everything OK at home?
C Fine. The children are in bed. Is it nice? What sort of place is it?
D It's a beautiful place in the mountains. We're staying in a hotel outside the town. It's a big chalet. The town is very small and modern. There's lots of snow for skiing and it's very sunny.
C Are your parents enjoying themselves?
D Oh, yes. They're having a wonderful time. But they're very tired. The journey was quite long. Mother is sleeping at the moment and father is having a drink in the bar. We're going to a restaurant this evening. And tomorrow we're going skiing.
C Well, have a good holiday. See you next week. Bye.
D Bye Jim.

Lesson 16 Vocabulary and Sounds, activity 3

1 Where were you born?
2 What were you like at school?
3 Who was your best friend at school?
4 What were you good at?
5 Were you often in trouble at school?

Lesson 16 Listening, activity 1

A Hello Jenny. You're home! How was your holiday?
B It was great. I was away for a week.
A Where were you?
B On the south coast.
A Who were you with?
B I was with two friends from college.
A Were you in a good hotel?
B Yes, it was all right. It was in the centre and there was a good view of the sea.
A What was the weather like?
B It wasn't very good. It was nice and warm on Monday and Friday and very cold on the other days.
A What about the food? Was that good?
B Yes, it was excellent.

Lesson 17 Grammar and Listening, activity 4

WOMAN I'd like some vegetable soup with bread, please.
WAITER I'm afraid we haven't got any soup today, madam. But we've got some potato salad.
WOMAN I don't like salads. I'll have a cheese omelette.
WAITER Cheese omelette. And for the main course?
WOMAN Roast chicken with boiled potatoes.
WAITER I'm sorry, but we haven't got any chicken. But you can have a steak. And there is pasta or chips instead of boiled potatoes.
WOMAN All right. A steak and chips. Have you got any wine or is there only water or tea?
WAITER Of course, madam. We've got some good Bulgarian red wine.
WOMAN Haven't you got any white wine?
WAITER Yes. It's German.
WOMAN That's fine. And cheese. I'd like some cheese and an ice cream.
WAITER Do you want any water?
WOMAN Yes, please. A bottle of spring water.

Lesson 18 Listening, activity 2

Conversation 1

WOMAN There's an interesting article about Kevin Costner. He was born in Los

Angeles in 1955.

MAN He's younger than me!

WOMAN And richer! The article says he studied business at the University of California. That's probably why he's rich!

MAN He didn't study acting, then?

WOMAN Yes. He went to drama school after university.

MAN When did he make his first film?

WOMAN In 1981 he appeared in a film for the first time. And in 1982 he directed his first film.

MAN He received an Oscar for *Dances with Wolves* in 1990. The Oscar for the best director.

WOMAN That was a very good film. He also appeared in *The Bodyguard* with Whitney Houston.

MAN That's right. In 1992. It was a good film, too, but it didn't receive any awards.

WOMAN After that he appeared in *Robin Hood*.

MAN The last film he made was *Waterworld*. That was a very expensive film.

Conversation 2

WOMAN What's the name of the American actress who appeared in *Silence of the Lambs* with Anthony Hopkins?

MAN Jodie Foster. It was a very good film. Very frightening.

WOMAN She received an Oscar for it, didn't she?

MAN Yes. The Oscar for the best actress. It was in 1990. She was quite young. She was born in 1962.

WOMAN But it wasn't her first Oscar, was it?.

MAN No. She received the award in 1988 for the film *The Accused*.

WOMAN Did she study drama?

MAN Yes. She went to Yale University.

WOMAN When did she start acting?

MAN Well, I suppose you can say that she started when she was three years old. She appeared in a television advertisement for sun cream! And then she played in *Taxi Driver* with Robert de Niro when she was only 12 years old.

WOMAN Was she the actress in *Maverick*? That was another good film.

MAN That's right. She played with Mel Gibson. She created her own production company in 1991. And she directs films now.

Lesson 19 Listening, activity 1

Description 1

Attention please, attention please. A little boy of about two years old is looking for his parents. He's got short, dark hair. He's wearing a blue sweater, yellow shorts and white trainers. He says his name is Tom and his baby sister's name is Sally. Can the parents of this little boy please come to the information desk near the entrance immediately? Thank you.

Description 2

A Don't you remember her? She was a very small girl, with long dark hair. She was always on her own. I don't think she had many friends at school. She was very hard working and very good at art. I think she lived in the country.

B Yes, I do remember her. She was very quiet and polite. She didn't talk very much. And she sat at the back of the class in the corner.

A That's right. Well I met her yesterday. She is completely different. She's tall and slim. She's got short fair hair and she wears glasses. She talks a lot now. The change is extraordinary. She was wearing very smart clothes. She was very friendly and we talked a lot about our schooldays.

Description 3

This police announcement is for people in the Halifax area. A dangerous man attacked an elderly couple in the street yesterday. He's about twenty-five. He is medium-height and very thin. He's got short, fair hair and a moustache. He is wearing jeans, a green sweater and a black jacket. He is very dangerous. If you see anyone who looks like this, phone the police immediately. Don't speak to the man, just go to the nearest phone and dial 999.

Lesson 22 Listening

MAN By the way, do you remember Janet Finch? She was at school with us.

WOMAN Yes, of course! What about her?

MAN I met her yesterday at the supermarket.

WOMAN Oh, how is she? The last time I saw her was about ten years ago.

MAN She looked very well. She lived in Italy from 1985 to 1988. She was a teacher in Milan.

WOMAN When did she come back to Britain?

MAN Last year. She spent two months in Coventry, then she moved to Cambridge in the spring.

Lesson 23 Listening, activity 2

The first model is wearing a red skirt. It's very short and shiny. She is wearing matching red and green shoes and a pink sweater. Her hair is orange and she's got small, purple John Lennon sunglasses. The general effect is strange but quite exciting. It will probably be a big success with young people.

The second model is wearing a classic outfit. Very suitable for the business woman. Smart but not too formal. She's got attractive grey trousers, a short yellow jacket over a grey and yellow blouse. She's wearing black boots and she's carrying a matching black bag.

The third model is wearing a long, blue evening dress. The dress is open on one side. She's wearing brown shoes and a small pink scarf. She's carrying a matching blue jacket. The general effect is very sophisticated and quite formal.

The last model is wearing a sports outfit. She's got black jeans with orange socks over the bottom of the jeans. She's got a pair of black trainers. She's wearing a green T-shirt with a black motif on the front. She's carrying a black jacket over her shoulder. A very practical outfit.

Lesson 24 Listening, activity 1

A How are you Betty? And how's Chris? Is he still working for that building company?

B No, Chris stopped work last month. He's sixty-five, you know.

A Goodness! So you're both on holiday all the time now! Have you got any plans?

B Well, first, we're going to have a long holiday. Next summer we're going on a two-month trip.

A Where are you going to?

B Central and South America.

A How wonderful! And are you going to stay here in London or are you going to move to the country?

B We're going to stay here. It's our home. All our friends live in London. And there's a lot to do. But we're going to change flats. This one is too big for two. We're going to buy a small flat near the park. But what about you and John? When are you going to stop work?

A Not for another two years, I'm afraid. I'm looking forward to retiring, but John isn't. He enjoys his job so much.

Lesson 25 Reading and Listening, activity 2

Dialogue 1

A Look, there are some seats over there.

B You two go and sit down and I'll get the orders. What would you like?

A I'd like a gin and orange, please.

B Would you like ice with your gin?

A No, thank you.

C And I'd like a Coke, please. No ice.

B Would you like anything to eat?

A No, thanks.

C I'd like a sandwich, please.

Dialogue 2

A Would you like some potatoes with your steak?

B No thanks, but can I have some more beans, please?

A Yes, help yourself. But leave some for your sister.

B Can I get the tomato ketchup?

A Yes, it's in the cupboard. Can you bring me a beer from the kitchen?

B Is there any mustard?

A Yes. It's in the fridge.

Lesson 26 Listening and Functions, activity 1

A Can I help you, sir?

B Yes. I'm looking for a winter coat.

A Are you looking for something fashionable or a classic style?

B I don't really know. Can you show me what you've got?

A Yes, they're over here.

B Can I try this dark blue one on?

A Yes, of course.

B It doesn't fit me. It's too big. Can I try a smaller size?

A I'm afraid we haven't got a size 40 in blue, sir. Would you like to try the dark green one?

B No, green doesn't suit me. This black one is very nice. It fits very well. I'll take it. How much is it?

A £150, sir. It's an excellent quality coat.

B Oh dear. That's very expensive. I think I'll leave it.

Lesson 28 Grammar and Functions, activity 3

MAN Are you all right?
WOMAN No, I don't feel very well.
MAN What's the matter?
WOMAN I feel sick.
MAN Oh dear!
WOMAN And I've got a headache.
MAN Have you got a temperature?
WOMAN I think so. I feel very hot.

Lesson 29 Vocabulary and Sounds, activity 4

1 The average temperature in Thailand in January is 25°C.
2 The highest point in Great Britain is 1,343 metres.
3 The average annual rainfall in the UK is 600 millimetres.
4 The UK covers a land area of 242,429 square kilometres.
5 The maximum speed on motorways in France is 130 kilometres per hour.
6 New York City's coastline is 920 kilometres long.
7 One litre of water weighs 1 kilogram.

Lesson 32 Listening, activity 2

MAN Have you ever been to Switzerland?
WOMAN No. I've never been there. But I'd like to go. What about you? Have you been?
MAN Yes. I have. I went two years ago for a skiing holiday.
WOMAN Was it very beautiful?
MAN Wonderful. Very beautiful mountain scenery. And the chocolate was delicious!
WOMAN I have been to Russia. I've visited Moscow and St Petersburg. They're beautiful cities. I went to Moscow in the winter. It was very cold.
MAN Did you visit Red Square?
WOMAN Yes, of course.
MAN I'd like to go to Australia.
WOMAN It's great. Beautiful weather. And wonderful beaches for surfing. I'd like to live there.
MAN Oh, you've been there, have you?
WOMAN Yes. I went for two weeks last winter to stay with relatives.
MAN Did you see any kangaroos?
WOMAN Yes. But only in a zoo!

Lesson 33 Reading and Listening, activity 2

JAN Hi, Pete!
PETE Oh, hello, Jan. Have you had a good day?
JAN Great! I've been at the office all day and I've met the new director.What about you? You look very tired. What sort of day have you had?
PETE Awful! I've only just finished the housework.
JAN Oh dear. I am sorry.
PETE I'm afraid, I haven't taken the car to the garage yet.
JAN That doesn't matter. I can take it tomorrow.
PETE Are you very hungry? I haven't made dinner yet.
JAN Oh ... Well, have you done any shopping?
PETE I'm sorry, I haven't had time.
JAN Well, how about going out to eat?
PETE That's a great idea!

Lesson 34 Listening, activity 1

Conversation 1

A So, you're going to Africa for your holiday, are you?
B That's right. We're leaving at the weekend.
A Where are you going in Africa?
B To Kenya. We've got a flight to Nairobi.
A Is that where you can see wild animals like elephants and giraffes?
B Yes. That's why we are going to Kenya.
A Great! Have a good time.

Conversation 2

A What time is it, Jim?
B Half past three.
A Oh dear! I'm going to be late.
A Where are you going?
B To the airport.
A What for?
B To meet my sister. Have you forgotten?

Conversation 3

A Hi! When did you get home?
B About ten minutes ago.
A Have you been into town?
B No, I haven't had time.
A Never mind. What time is it now?
B Five o'clock.
A Well, we need some food for this evening. I'll go to the supermarket now.
B And I'll cook dinner!

Conversation 4

A Have you got the tickets for Eurostar yet?
B I didn't have time to get them this morning.
A Have you phoned the station?
B Yes. They are ready. I need to go and get them.
A Well, I can go now if you like.
B Thank you. That would be great. I don't really have time.

Lesson 35 Listening, activity 1

MAN What are you really good at?
WOMAN Not very many things, I'm afraid. I can swim quite well, but not very fast.
MAN Isn't there anything you can do well?
WOMAN Yes. I'm quite a good dancer. I go to dancing lessons once a week.
MAN What type of dancing?
WOMAN Modern dancing. It's wonderful.
MAN Is there anything you do really badly?
WOMAN Lots of things. I'm a terrible cook. I don't like cooking. I always buy pre-cooked food. I can't sing. I'm also a very bad driver. I go too fast in town and too slowly on the motorway.
MAN Oh dear. You sound like a dangerous driver!
WOMAN I certainly am.

Lesson 36 Grammar and Listening, activity 4

MAN What have you decided to do tomorrow?
WOMAN Well, first I'll get up very early and have a big breakfast. Then, I think I'll go sightseeing.
MAN What do you want to see?
WOMAN Lots of things. I think I'll go to the Louvre first. Then I'll visit Notre Dame Cathedral.
MAN Will you come back to the hotel for lunch?
WOMAN I'm sorry, I won't have time. I'd like to have lunch on a boat on the River Seine.
MAN That sounds great!
WOMAN Then in the afternoon I'll go up the Eiffel Tower to get a view of Paris, visit the Montmartre district, go shopping for souvenirs on the Champs Elysées, have a glass of wine in a cafe and ...
MAN That sounds like a very busy day!

Lesson 37 Sounds

11° -1° 16° 35° -4° 24° -10°

Lesson 37 Reading and Listening, activity 2

MAN I saw a programme about life in the future on television last night. It was very gloomy.
WOMAN Well, I think life in the future will be terrible. There will be too many people in the world and not enough food for everyone.
MAN You're worse than the people on the TV! I think life will be better than today. People will be more healthy. And they'll live longer and happier lives.
WOMAN You're very optimistic. But I think you are wrong. I think life will be very hard for most people.

Lesson 38 Sounds, activity 1

1 Tea is grown in Brazil.
No, it isn't. It's grown in India.
2 The telephone was invented by Marconi.
No, it wasn't. It was invented by Bell.
3 *Guernica* was painted by Monet.
No, it wasn't. It was painted by Picasso.
4 *Hamlet* was written by Spencer.
No, it wasn't. It was written by Shakespeare.
5 Toyota cars are made in the United States.
No, they aren't. They're made in Japan.
6 The Pyramids were built by Alexander the Great. No, they weren't. They were built by the Pharaohs

Lesson 39 Listening and Reading, activity 1

Phone call 1

A Can I speak to Peter, please? This is John Griffiths.
B I'm sorry, he's out at the moment. Can I take a message?
A Yes, please. It's about the concert tonight. I've got the tickets for us. It's at the Palace Hall. It starts at 8.30 so we want to be there for 8.15. There's a train which leaves here at 7.15. I think it's easier than in the car.
B Right. I've got that. Do you want him to ring you back?

A No. I'm out until this evening, so there's no point.
B OK. Goodbye.
A Thank you. Goodbye.

Phone call 2

C Hi, Marjorie! Is Liz there, please? This is Maria.
D I'm sorry, Maria, but she's out just now. Can I help?
C Well, you see, I'm supposed to meet her for lunch tomorrow. The trouble is I've got an appointment at the dentist's at 1.30. But I can meet her earlier for coffee – say 11 o'clock.
D OK. I'll leave her a message.
C So, if she doesn't ring me back, I'll see her at Ascari's at 11. Oh, before I forget. Tell her I've got her books she needs for college. And they aren't expensive, only £5 each.
D Right. Goodbye, Maria.
C Thanks. Bye.

Phone call 3

E Hello. Can I speak to Henry Croft, please? This is Helen Croft speaking.
F Oh, hello, Mrs Croft. I'm afraid your husband is in a meeting at the moment. Would you like to leave a message?
E Yes, please. Can you tell him that I'm at Charles de Gaulle Airport in Paris and my flight is delayed. I don't know what time it will arrive in London. He doesn't need to meet me at Heathrow. I'll get a taxi.
F I've noted that down.
E Oh, by the way. Tell him the new office in Paris is fine and the new manager seems very competent.
F Right. Goodbye Mrs Croft.
E Goodbye.

Phone call 4

G Hello, this is John. Can I speak to Anna, please?
H I'm afraid she's out. Can I give her a message?
G That would be great. Tell her there's an interesting flat for sale in Fulham. It's quite a nice area: not noisy. It's near a tube station and a small shopping centre. There's a park not far away. It isn't very expensive. If she wants to see it, I'm free tomorrow afternoon.
H Right. I've got that. Anything else?
G Umm. I'm at the office this afternoon if she wants to give me a ring.

Answer Key

Lesson 1

VOCABULARY

1 Rome, Italy; Rio de Janeiro, Brazil; Washington, the United States of America; Moscow, Russia; Sydney, Australia; Istanbul, Turkey
2 *Across:* Spain India Argentina Turkey Canada Brazil
Down: Peru Japan Greece France China Italy Russia Korea Britain Mexico Thailand
3 1 Seoul is in Korea. 2 Buenos Aires is in Argentina. 3 Paris is in France. 4 Tokyo is in Japan. 5 Athens is in Greece. 6 Lima is in Peru.

FUNCTIONS

1 1 What is your name? 2 Where are you from? 3 My name is Charlie. 4 I am from Canada. 5 Is your name Maria?
2 1 b 2 c 5 a
4 *Verbs:* is am are be
Subject pronouns: you I

SOUNDS

1 Japan China Canada Korea Germany Russia Brazil Turkey Ukraine Morocco

2

oO	Oo	Ooo	oOo
Japan	China	Canada	Korea
Brazil	Russia	Germany	Morocco
Ukraine	Turkey		

LISTENING

1 A 2 B 3 C 4 D 1
2 *Conversation 1:* France, Spain
Conversation 2: Italy, the United States of America
Conversation 3: Sweden, Canada
Conversation 4: Australia

Lesson 2

VOCABULARY

1 *Jobs:* teacher waiter receptionist doctor chef actor artist police officer nurse journalist
2 1 He's a waiter. 2 She's an artist. 3 He's a chef. 4 She's a doctor. 5 He's a farmer. 6 They're police officers.
3 1 her 2 Moscow 3 we 4 Brazil 5 friend 6 your

GRAMMAR

1 1 They're 2 You're 3 Their 4 your 5 Their
2 1 He's 2 His 3 He's 4 his 5 He's
3 1 She's a secretary. 2 They're from Australia. 3 He's an actor. 4 They're doctors. 5 We're farmers.
4 1 He is 2 They are 3 I am 4 We are 5 They are 6 She is

READING

1 1 Maria is a receptionist.
2 Jim is a jazz musician.
3 Isabella is an economist.
4 Yannick is a journalist.
5 Emma is a nurse.
2 1 No, he is from France.
2 No, she is from Milan.
3 No, she is a nurse.
4 No, he is a jazz musician.
5 No, they are teachers.
3 His name is Yannick. He's from France. He's a journalist for an international magazine. His wife's name is Isabella and she's from Barcelona. She's an economist.

LISTENING

1 I'm from Britain.
I'm a computer technician here at the university.
I'm from Vancouver in Canada.
I'm a student.
France teacher
2 His name's Silvio.
Where's he from?
He's from Italy. What's his job?
He's an accountant.

Lesson 3

VOCABULARY

1 *Nouns:* student children Japan doctor surname phone number brother actor friend address first name job boyfriend
Adjectives: married single good-looking

GRAMMAR

1 1 c 2 d 3 e 4 a 5 f 6 b
2 1 Where 2 How 3 What 4 Who 5 Where 6 What
4 *Suggested answers*
1 Is she married? 2 Are you single? 3 Are his children students? 4 Is he from Oxford? 5 Are you an economist? 6 Is she a teacher?
5 1 No, she isn't. She's from Romania. 2 No, he isn't. He's a nurse. 3 No, they aren't. They're Argentinian. 4 No, she isn't. She's seventeen. 5 No, he isn't. He's married.

LISTENING

1 at a job interview
2 What's your name? What's your job? How old are you? Are you married? Are you British?
3 1 No, she isn't. She's single.
2 No, she isn't. She's 25.
3 No, she isn't. She's Italian.

WRITING

1 Picture A: Janvi Singh
Picture C: May Downs
Picture D: Michael Haines

Lesson 4

VOCABULARY

1 1 room 2 chair 3 interesting 4 that
3 1 kind/good 2 good/kind 3 interesting 4 comfortable 5 beautiful

GRAMMAR AND SOUNDS

1 43 13 97 56 51 12 63 17 8 94 77 15 85 3 39
2 classrooms teachers addresses numbers colleges classes chairs
3 1 There is 2 There are 3 There is 4 There are 5 There is
4 /θ/: thirteen three thanks think /ð/: this their with there the they

READING

1 It is a bilingual school.
2 new bilingual old modern big friendly good big comfortable special small expensive
3 1 No, it isn't. 2 It's for children. 3 They are six and nine years old. 4 It's in the town centre. 5 It's an old building but inside it's modern.

Lesson 5

VOCABULARY

1 *Electronic products:* calculator camera computer mobile phone personal stereo radio
Office things: calculator computer diary notebook pen pencil
Jobs: accountant doctor farmer vet
Places: city country library school
2 A keys B diary C comb D calculator E glasses F credit card G gloves H brush I watch J camera
3 A near B in C under D on
4 1 How 2 What 3 What 4 Where

GRAMMAR

1 1 He has got 2 They have got 3 She is 4 I have got 5 She has got 6 He is

SOUNDS

1 1 wallet 2 colour 3 comb 4 camera 5 watch 6 diary

LISTENING

glasses colour blue green bag on under

Lesson 6

VOCABULARY

1

Male	**Female**
man	woman
boy	girl
father	mother
brother	sister
nephew	niece
son	daughter
husband	wife
uncle	aunt
grandfather	grandmother
cousin	cousin

2 1 aunt 2 niece 3 grandmother 4 son 5 brother 6 cousin
3 men women children families people wives countries

READING AND GRAMMAR

2 *Family A:* Jenny is thirty-two years old and has got a job in a post office in a small village. She's divorced and has got an eight-year-old daughter, Cilla, and a three-year-old son, Jamie. She's got a small house with a big garden in the village. She's got a lot of friends in the village. Jenny's mother, Kate, lives in the same village. She helps Jenny with the children when she's at work.
3 1 Jenny is divorced. (Elizabeth's husband is Peter.) 2 Elizabeth has a part-time job in a school. (Peter is an architect.) 3 Peter has got four children. (Jenny has got two children.) 4 Jenny has got a job in a post office. (Elizabeth has got a part-time job in a school.) 5 Jenny has got a house in a village. (Peter and Elizabeth have got a house near London.)
4 1 Elizabeth is Peter's wife.
2 Fiona and Michael are Peter's parents.
3 Cilla is Jenny's daughter/Kate's granddaughter/Jamie's sister.
4 Jamie is Jenny's son/Kate's grandson/Cilla's brother.

LISTENING

1 Speaker 1: Helen
Speaker 2: Greg
2 1 teacher 2 two 3 American 4 computer 6 married

Lesson 7

VOCABULARY

1 1 It's twenty past four in the afternoon.
2 It's a quarter to eleven in the morning.
3 It's nine o'clock in the evening.
4 It's half past eleven in the morning.
5 It's a quarter past six in the morning.
2 1 get up 2 have breakfast 3 start work 4 have lunch 5 finish work 6 have dinner 7 go to bed

READING

1 *Prepositions of time:* at nine in the morning; at five in the evening; at eight; at five; at weekends; on Saturday mornings; on Wednesday afternoons; at lunchtime; at midday; In the evening; at about eight o'clock

GRAMMAR

1 1 in 2 at 3 at 4 at 5 in 6 on 7 at 8 on

SOUNDS

1 1 Do you work at the weekend?
2 Do people work on Sunday mornings?
3 Do they have lunch at home?
4 Do we finish work at five today?
5 Do you have a siesta in the afternoon?
2 1 work 2 clock 3 girl 4 breakfast
3 1 3.30 2 10.15 3 7.45 4 2.10 5 9.55 6 1.35 7 11.30 8 7.00 9 4.05 10 6.40

Lesson 8

GRAMMAR

1 1 are 2 is 3 are 4 aren't 5 Are 6 isn't 7 Is 8 is
2 1 any 2 some 3 some 4 any 5 any 6 some

LISTENING

1 *Speaker 1:* study
Speaker 2: sitting room
Speaker 3: bedroom
2 *Room 1:* 1 study 2 upstairs, bathroom 3 bookcases 4 window, computer 5 mirror, armchair
Room 2: 1 sitting room 2 window, garden 3 sofa, fire 4 curtains, piano 5 television, video
Room 3: 1 bedroom 2 upstairs 3 bed, lamp 4 cupboard 5 plants

SOUNDS

1 /ɑː/: armchair bath carpet garden large plant
/eɪ/: bookcase game plane radio table washbasin

WRITING AND READING

2 Italy
3 1 F 2 T 3 F 4 F 5 T

Lesson 9

LISTENING

1 *Across:* relax live watch get drink make play do go eat sing
Down: read learn wash work have see come like start finish
2 1 have 2 watch 3 make 4 eat, drink 5 play 6 learn

GRAMMAR

1 1 He/She has a sauna on Wednesday evenings. 2 He/She watches sport on television on Saturday afternoons. 3 He/She makes the Sunday lunch for the family. 4 He/She eats a sandwich and drinks mineral water for lunch. 5 He/She plays the guitar in a rock band with friends. 6 He/She learns Spanish at evening classes.
2 1 Where 2 How 3 Who 4 What 5 When

READING

1 a man
2 He makes dinner. He watches the sport on television. He goes running. He reads. He watches television.
3 She goes to language classes. She goes to a friend's house for dinner. She works on her computer.
4 They have a drink. They sit and have dinner in front of the television. They go to the cinema. They have a drink in a bar. They get up at midday. They go to the supermarket. They go to a restaurant or to a nightclub. They go to her parents' house.

LISTENING

1 *Woman 1:* has a cup of tea; makes dinner; goes to a friend's house; goes running; goes to a jazz club
Woman 2: reads the newspaper; has a language class; has dinner with a friend; works on her computer
2 Woman 2

SOUNDS

1 1 gets 2 has 3 makes 4 speaks

Lesson 10

SOUNDS

1 *Two syllables:* football country singer tennis programme skating
Three syllables: computer magazine unemployed afternoon cinema classical

READING

1 c 2 d 3 e 4 a 5 b

GRAMMAR

1

Subject	**Object**
I	me
you	you
he	him
she	her
it	it
we	us
they	them

2 1 it 2 them 3 it 4 her 5 them 6 him
3 1 Do you like classical music?
2 What type of music do you like?
3 I do not like skiing at all.
4 Do you like going to the cinema?
5 I do not like it very much.
4 1 I like eating Chinese food.
2 I like watching television.
3 I like going to the cinema.
4 I like playing computer games.
5 I like drinking tea.

LISTENING

1 1a 2b
2 *Man:* modern art, classical art, classical music
Woman: classical art, reggae, dancing

Lesson 11

VOCABULARY AND GRAMMAR

1 late punctual early on time

SOUNDS

2 *Happy:* Sentences 1 and 6
Unhappy: Sentences 2, 3, 4, and 5

LISTENING

1 *Suggested answers*
taxi driver: car city streets map nightwork drive
teacher: classroom pupils school desk folder teach
chef: food restaurant dinner cook lunch
musician: dancing club guitar rock concert play
2 *Suggested answers*
a teacher b musician c chef d taxi driver

3 *Speaker 1:* musician
Speaker 2: chef
4 *Musician:* Sentences 1, 4, 6 and 7
Chef: Sentences 2, 5, 8 and 10
5 teacher
6 1 get up 2 have 3 leaves
4 read 5 leave 6 have
7 works 8 get 9 go 10 get

Lesson 12

READING

1 Picture A
2 many journeys take a day; there is a bus only once or twice a week; dangerous; break down; very slow and uncomfortable; very crowded
3 It is cheap.

GRAMMAR

1 1 a bus – buses
2 a coach – coaches
3 a ferry – ferries
4 an airport – airports
5 a house – houses
6 an office – offices
7 a delay – delays
8 an hour – hours
2 1 the, the 2 - 3 a 4 - 5 a
6 the 7 a, a 8 The 9 - 10 the, -
3 *Suggested answers*
1 How long does it take?
2 How do you get to work?
3 Do you go very often?
4 How much is it?
5 How far is it?

SOUNDS

1 1 It's about eighty miles.
2 The office is near the station.
3 It's the age of the train.
4 It's quite expensive.
People sit on the roof
2 slow coach train plane
bus month drive ride
stop long quick live

Lesson 13

VOCABULARY AND GRAMMAR

1 *Across:* 3 swim 6 cook 8 drink
9 be 12 do 13 ride 17 read
18 win 19 fly
Down: 1 ski 2 hold 4 walk
5 meet 7 knit 10 go 11 drive
14 draw 15 eat 16 play 17 run
2 1 can't 2 can 3 can, can't 4 can
5 can, can't

SOUNDS

1 cupboard daylight foreign hour knit listen night often walk write
2 1✗ 2✓ 3✗ 4✗ 5✗ 6✓

READING AND WRITING

1 A camera B bed C television
D dishwasher E mirror F fire
2 1 dishwasher 2 bed 3 television
4 camera 5 fire 6 mirror
3 is can wash sleep lie put on watch use take carry sit look see
4 1 It is usually in the kitchen.
2 It is often upstairs in a house.
3 This is often in the sitting room.
4 ...you can carry it in your bag.
5 It is often in the sitting room.
6 It can be on a wall in any room in the house. There is always one in the bathroom.

Lesson 14

VOCABULARY

1 send eat buy take out change
2 *Post office:* stamps send buy letters envelopes
Newsagent's: buy magazine newspaper sweets
Chemist's: sun cream medicine buy aspirin
Bank: account money traveller's cheques take out change
Station: buy platform ticket train
Restaurant: meal menu buy dinner eat

GRAMMAR AND READING

2 in the west; at the end; in; inthe middle; behind; opposite; opposite; between; Behind; in; opposite; At the end; on the same side; on the corner; opposite; out of
3 1 museum 2 chemist's 3 tourist information centre 4 post office
5 indoor market 6 shopping mall
7 park 8 hotel 9 bank
4 1 opposite 2 between
3 opposite 4 on the corner of
5 behind 6 next to, opposite

LISTENING

1 1 stamps, the post office
2 aspirin, a chemist's
3 an Italian restaurant
2 *Conversation 1:* 1 along 2 right, straight ahead 3 opposite, behind
Conversation 2: 1 along
2 opposite 3 on the left
3 husband French restaurant twenty minutes' ten metres next to Italian

Lesson 15

GRAMMAR

1 enjoying staying passing having living learning shopping sitting flying travelling taking lying writing
2 1 are staying 2 is lying
3 are having 4 are flying
5 are enjoying

SOUNDS

1 *Two syllables:* ugly lively modern mountains boring
Three syllables: beautiful attractive wonderful
Four syllables: industrial
2 1 We're having a wonderful time.
2 I'm not enjoying the flight.
3 She's learning to swim.
4 They're staying at an expensive hotel.
5 He's travelling for his job.
6 I'm writing this on the beach.

VOCABULARY

beautiful – ugly; east – west; interesting – boring; old-fashioned – modern; north– south; cold – hot; dark – light; quiet – noisy

LISTENING

1 *Picture A:* sea coast port
Picture B: chalet skiing mountains snow cold holiday
Picture C: modern industrial town river
2 *Suggested answers*
Picture A: lively interesting
Picture B: beautiful
Picture C: ugly
3 *Conversation 1:* city sea-port
Conversation 2: mountain ski resort
4 *Conversation 1:* 1 false (her mother) 2 false (in the centre)
3 true 4 true
Conversation 2: 1 false (her husband) 2 true 3 true
4 false (her mother is sleeping, her father is having a drink)

READING AND WRITING

1 It is on the Mediterranean coast in the south-east of France near Italy. It is between the mountains and the sea.
2 beautiful location pleasant climate gambling casinos motor race no taxes

Lesson 16

VOCABULARY AND READING

1 1 d 2 a 3 c 4 b
2 *dog:* noisy naughty not obedient
girlfriend: shy attractive
girlfriend's hair: dark
weather on caravan holiday: horrid
holiday in Greece: exciting wonderful
children: not well-behaved
parents: bad-tempered
caravan holiday: terrible
weather in Greece: hot

GRAMMAR

1 1 was 2 were 3 was
4 were 5 were 6 was
2 1 Where were you born?
2 What were you like at school?
3 Who was your best friend at school?
4 What were you good at?
5 Were you often in trouble in school?

VOCABULARY AND SOUNDS

1 stubborn obedient lazy cheerful horrid untidy polite naughty disappointing

LISTENING

1 1 b 2 a 3 f 4 c 5 e 6 d

Lesson 17

VOCABULARY

1 1 rice 2 bacon 3 potato
4 oil 5 salt 6 onion

READING AND WRITING

1 1 true 2 false 3 false
4 false 5 true 6 true
7 true 8 false
2 *common:* chopsticks with the Chinese population; smoking
crowded, noisy and hot: restaurants in the early evening
relaxed: restaurants
3 *C:* table meal spoon fingers restaurants
U: food salt fish sauce alcohol drink
4 2 Only the Chinese population use chopsticks.
3 They use their fingers.
4 They can drink alcohol.
8 Restaurants are very informal.

GRAMMAR AND LISTENING

1 *U:* wine oil yoghurt butter pork milk water beef bread tea salt rice soup pasta cheese
C: apple egg onion lemon carrot steak
2 1 some 2 some 3 a
4 any 5 some 6 a
3 at a restaurant
4 1 some 2 any 3 some
4 a 5 any 6 a
7 any 8 some 9 any
10 some 11 an/some 12 any

Lesson 18

VOCABULARY

1 1 hit 2 teenager 3 album
4 musician 5 group 6 award
7 guitar
2 1 g 2 d 3 a 4 f
5 c 6 h 7 e 8 b

GRAMMAR AND READING

1 appeared created died learned lived composed married moved played started worked finished
2 1 married 2 appeared/played
3 learned 4 worked 5 started
6 created
3 1 learned 2 started
3 appeared/played 4 lived
5 moved 6 moved 7 married
8 worked 9 composed 10 died

SOUNDS

1 1 talked 2 appeared 3 visited
4 watched
2 1 She was born in London.
2 He learned to play the piano.
3 She received an award.
4 They created the group *The Police*.
5 He started work as a teacher.

LISTENING

2 1 Kevin Costner 2 Jodie Foster
3 1 was born 2 studied
3 received 4 appeared
5 appeared

Lesson 19

VOCABULARY

2 *Suggested answers*
Picture A: curly glasses
Picture B: middle-aged well-built dark
Picture C: elderly fair curly

3 *Suggested answers*
Picture A: The woman has straight hair. She doesn't have glasses
Picture B: The man is young and slim. He has fair hair.
Picture C: The woman is young/middle-aged. She has dark straight hair.

FUNCTIONS

1 *Suggested answers*
1 What's he like?
2 What does she look like?
3 How tall is she?
4 How old is he?
5 Who does she look like?
6 How does she dress?

SOUNDS

/ɪ/: built slim thin sixty
/aɪ/: kind time nice smile polite child

LISTENING

1 1 a lost child 2 an old classmate 3 a criminal
2 1 two 2 short, dark 3 blue, yellow, white
3 2 3 6

Lesson 20

VOCABULARY

1 *Across:* did made bought took said lost went spent became
Down: found had gave got came wrote
2 1 wrote 2 did/bought 3 went 4 took/got 5 made 6 lost
3 1 b 2 e 3 f 4 a 5 c 6 d

GRAMMAR

1 1 Did you visit a museum yesterday?
2 Did you write some postcards at the weekend?
3 Did you do some shopping yesterday?
4 Did you go to a restaurant on Saturday?
5 Did you take a train last week?

READING

1 1 Diana. 2 She is writing to Robert. 3 No, she is travelling with Mike.
2 1 It was sunny and warm.
2 She spent four days in London.
3 She took the Eurostar to Paris.
4 She stayed with her cousin.
5 She lost her passport in the Metro.
6 She went to Barcelona after Paris.
7 She stayed in a hotel.
8 She spent two days by the sea.

SOUNDS

1 good 2 close 3 born 4 give 5 have

Lesson 21

GRAMMAR AND VOCABULARY

1 encouraged informed thought sold married left found refused
2 1 c 2 d 3 e 4 g 5 b 6 a 7 f

SOUNDS

1 and 2 *Two syllables:* divorced explain famous final happen inform notice refuse
Three syllables: continue disappear encourage successful

READING

1 William Shakespeare
was was went married had left went did lived worked stopped was wrote wrote finished left went died
2 2 When was he born?
3 Where did he go to school?
4 Who did he marry?
5 Where did he work as an actor?
6 When did he stop acting?
7 Why did he stop acting?
8 When did he write his first play?
9 Where did he go in 1612?
10 When did he die?
3 Between 1585 and 1590.
4 1 He was born in Stratford.
2 He was born in 1564.
3 He went to the local grammar school.
4 He married Anne Hathaway.
5 He worked in London.
6 He stopped acting in 1603.
7 Because he was famous for his writing.
8 He wrote his first play in 1590–91.
9 He went back to Stratford.
10 He died in 1616.

WRITING

1 was went was lived went wrote was received
2 *Suggested answer*
Mark Twain was born in Missouri, USA in 1835. We know that he worked as a ship's pilot on the Mississippi in 1857 and he became a journalist in 1862. He went on a tour of Europe in 1865 and in 1876 he wrote The Adventures of Tom Sawyer. He died in 1910.

Lesson 22

VOCABULARY AND SOUNDS

1 fifth sixth eighth ninth twelfth thirteenth fifteenth
2 *Nouns:* discovery, discoverer explosion invention, inventor landing painting, painter take-off win, winner, winnings
3 1 won 2 discovered 3 exploded 4 painted 5 invented 6 landed

READING

1 B
2 *Columbia*, the first space shuttle took off.
Challenger exploded at take-off.
NASA put the Hubble Space Telescope into space.
Endeavor replaced *Challenger*.

GRAMMAR

1 in June, in 1995, in the evening, in the morning
on Friday, on the 26th March
at the weekend, at night
yesterday
night/evening/morning
last month/weekend/night
a month/week ago 10 years ago

LISTENING

1 1 yesterday 2 about ten years ago 3 1985 4 1988 5 Last year 6 two months 7 in the spring

Lesson 23

VOCABULARY

1 *Across:* 1 jacket 6 T-shirt 8 shoe 9 skirt 11 blouse
Down: 1 jeans 2 coat 3 trousers 4 shorts 5 suit 7 boots 8 sock 10 tie

LISTENING

1, 2 and 3 Model 1 (C): red skirt, pink sweater, purple sunglasses
Model 2 (B): grey trousers, yellow jacket, grey and yellow blouse
Model 3 (D): blue dress, brown shoes, pink scarf
Model 4 (A): black jeans, orange socks, black trainers, green T-shirt

READING AND GRAMMAR

1 1 Pat is writing to Sarah.
2 Pat is on holiday in New Zealand.
3 She is Pat's mother's cousin.
2 *Present continuous:* I'm having I'm staying she's having I'm staying I'm staying I'm flying
Present simple: she's Aunt Grace is She's got she wears she smiles she talks she is she reads she doesn't know she never goes she says it's she's we visit the scenery is
3 expensive – the trip to Britain
wonderful – her holiday
beautiful – the scenery
lovely – Aunt Grace's eyes
interesting – Aunt Grace
happy – Aunt Grace
4 1 are staying 2 live 3 wears 4 is looking 5 goes 6 is laughing

Lesson 24

VOCABULARY

1 1 study 2 stop 3 worry 4 save 5 spend 6 invite
2 1 d 2 f 3 e 4 b 5 a 6 c

GRAMMAR

1 *Suggested answers*
1 He's going to fly to Hawaii.
2 They're going to see a football match.
3 They're going to play tennis.
4 She's going to do the shopping.

SOUNDS

1 *Tick:* 2 4 *Cross:* 1 3 5

LISTENING

1 c
2 1 65 2 work 3 trip/holiday 4 Central and South America 5 move, London 6 flat, park

WRITING

1 magazine fashion writer
2 *Suggested answers*
On Monday she's going to visit the hat exhibition at the new art and design college at 2 pm.
On Tuesday at 7.15 am she's going to take the Eurostar to Paris. At 11 am she's going to do an interview with a Paris clothes designer.
On Wednesday she's going to an editorial meeting for the January edition of the magazine.
On Thursday she's going to the Piccadilly clothes show.
On Friday she's going to finish her article on hats.
On Saturday she's going to Pete and Jenny's party.
On Sunday she's going to visit her parents in Oxford.

Lesson 25

VOCABULARY

1 a waiter b bill c service, tip d starter e coffee f reservation g menu h course, dessert i taste j order
2 1 f 2 a 3 g 4 j 5 i 6 d 7 h 8 e 9 b 10 c

READING AND LISTENING

1 1 in a pub 2 at home
2 and 3 *Dialogue 1:* in the corner (over there) three (two)
gin and tonic (gin and orange)
Yes, please (No, thank you)
a mineral water (a Coke)
some crisps (a sandwich)
Dialogue 2: salad (potatoes)
chips (beans) fridge (cupboard)
glass of water (a beer)
I'm afraid there isn't any left
(Yes. It's in the fridge.)

FUNCTIONS

1 *Waiter:* 1 3 4 6
Customer: 2 5 7 8
2 *Suggested answers*
2 Certainly, madam.
3 I'd like salad, please.
4 Can I have a beer, please?
5 Certainly, sir.
6 Chocolate, please.
7 What flavour would you like?
8 Yes, sir.
3 *Suggested answers*
1 Would you like a dessert?
2 Can I have some chips, please?
3 What flavour would you like?
4 Can I help you?
5 Can you bring me the wine list, please?
6 Do you like the salad?

Lesson 26

GRAMMAR

1 yourself himself herself itself ourselves yourselves themselves
2 1 myself 2 themselves 3 himself 4 yourself 5 ourselves

3 *Suggested answers*
1 They enjoyed themselves at the party. 2 She is teaching herself to speak French. 3 He talks to himself.

VOCABULARY
1 newspaper toothpaste sunglasses handbag raincoat hamburger
3 a bottle of shampoo a packet of biscuits a box of matches a tube of toothpaste a bar of chocolate a can of tomatoes

SOUNDS
1 The first word is stressed.
2 1 too 2 like 3 suit 4 fit 5 colour

LISTENING AND FUNCTIONS
1 in a shop
2 and 3 1 False (He wants to buy a winter coat.) 2 True 3 True 4 False (It's too big.) 5 True 6 True 7 False (He doesn't buy it because it's expensive.)
4 1 I'll take it. 2 I think I'll leave it.

Lesson 27

VOCABULARY
1 *binoculars:* metal, plastic and glass
wallet: leather or plastic
umbrella: nylon and metal
book: paper
2 *Across:* 1 binoculars 3 umbrella 5 Property 8 wood 10 his 11 metal
Down: 1 box 2 camera 4 new 6 purse 7 thick 9 out

SOUNDS
2 1 your, his 2 your, hers 3 her, mine 4 their, ours 5 your, yours 6 our, theirs

GRAMMAR
1 *Suggested answers*
1 What shape is it?
2 What colour is it?
3 What's it made of?
4 Is this yours?
5 Whose books are they?
6 What's in your bag?
2 2 It's his. 3 It's theirs. 4 They're ours. 5 They're hers. 6 It's yours.

READING AND WRITING
1 3
2 A stamps, purse B umbrellas C papers, keys, phone card, cash card, bag, car keys
D nothing
D is the most careful.

Lesson 28

VOCABULARY
2 1 c 2 d 3 e 4 a 5 b
3 *Suggested answers*
1 I've got a sore throat.
2 My back hurts.
3 I feel faint.
4 I feel dizzy.
5 I've got a cough.

GRAMMAR AND FUNCTIONS
3 1 d 2 a 3 c 4 b

SOUNDS
2 *Two syllables:* aspirin medicine complaint private treatment
Three syllables: accident exercise hospital temperature

READING AND WRITING
1 A sun B insects
3 You shouldn't stay in the sun too long
you should stay out of the sun at midday
You should use suncream
you should lie down in a cool place
you should call a doctor
you should take medicine every day

Lesson 29

VOCABULARY AND SOUNDS
1 *Across:* long, good light dry big high slow hot fast easy small modern
Down: heavy bad low wet old dirty safe dark young cold
2 good – better – best
bad – worse – worst
heavy – heavier – heaviest
old – older – oldest
low – lower – lowest
easy – easier – easiest
big – bigger – biggest
wet – wetter – wettest
3 2 metre 3 millimetre 4 kilometres per hour 5 kilometre 6 square kilometre 7 kilogram 8 litre
4 1 25°C 2 1,343 m 3 600 mm 4 242,429 sq km 5 130 kph 6 920 km 7 1 kg

READING AND GRAMMAR
1 1 C 2 A 3 E 4 D 5 B
2 the world's fourth largest country; The world's second longest river; the world's widest river; it covers the largest area the country with the highest population
the 6th highest in the world; South America's biggest city; smaller than São Paulo; more densely populated; the warmest months; the most rainfall
3 *Suggested answers*
1 Brazil is smaller than Canada.
2 Brazil has a bigger population than Chile.
3 The Nile is narrower than the Amazon.
4 Rio is smaller than São Paulo.
5 Most Brazilians live in the cities or on the coast.
4 *Suggested answers*
1 Brazil is bigger than Argentina.
2 The Amazon is wider than the Nile.
3 Brazil has got a bigger population than Peru.
4 Rio is smaller than São Paulo.
5 June is colder than December.
5 1 Rio is not as big as São Paulo.
2 São Paulo is not as warm as Rio.
3 The climate in the Amazon basin is not as dry as the climate on the coast.
4 The Amazon is not as long as the Nile.
5 It is not as warm in June as it is in December.

Lesson 30

VOCABULARY
1 hang gliding motor racing windsurfing horse riding basketball

GRAMMAR
1 1 most 2 more 3 most 4 most 5 more 6 more

READING AND WRITING
1 2
2 more beautiful more civilised
more good-looking
more sophisticated
more mouthwatering
more exotic more exciting
more interesting
more expressive
more monumental
more spectacular
3 *Suggested answers*
Shops are more exciting.
The ringing of telephones is stranger.
Bread is tastier.
Shop assistants are more efficient.
Bank clerks are friendlier.
Children are politer.
Street signs are stranger.

Lesson 31

GRAMMAR
2 1 h 2 d 3 f 4 g 5 b 6 c 7 a 8 e
3 1 mustn't 2 mustn't 3 must 4 mustn't 5 mustn't 6 must 7 must 8 mustn't
4 rules

READING
1 A 1 B 4
2 *Suggested answers*
B: keep your dog on a lead
C: no golf.
D: no cycling.
E: put litter in bins
F: You are not allowed to sleep overnight on the benches.
3 You must wear proper swimsuits. An adult must stay with children under six at all times.
4 *Suggested answers*
Notice A
You must put litter in the bins.
You mustn't play golf.
You mustn't cycle.
You must keep your dog on a lead.
You mustn't sleep overnight on the benches.
You mustn't stay inside after closing time.
You mustn't walk on the flower beds.
You mustn't climb the trees.
Notice B
You mustn't wear shorts.
You mustn't run or jump.
You mustn't smoke in the pool area.
You mustn't eat or drink near the pool.

Lesson 32

READING
1 a waitress, an actress, a nanny, a ticket seller, a cook, a zoo-keeper, in telesales
2 Jane Brooks has had fifty-four jobs. still hasn't found her ideal career. She has been a model ... I just haven't found ...
3 The shortest she had was as a cook in a canteen. She left it after just two hours.
The longest job she had was as a zoo-keeper. She stayed in that job for two months.

GRAMMAR
1 *Past participle:* been drunk had driven read left flown taken bought made written sold fought met found eaten gone seen worn
Past simple: ate had read left saw wore bought made went sold fought met found took flew drove wrote
2 1 Have you ever been to a foreign country?
2 He has never appeared on television.
3 I have visited a lot of countries.
4 They went to Spain last year.
5 When did they go to Spain?
3 1 drunk 2 driven 3 met/seen 4 worn/made 5 flown/been 6 eaten/had 7 written 8 taken
4 1 have never been 2 went 3 has found 4 met 5 has never flown 6 drank
5 1 been, went 2 gone, gone, went

LISTENING
2 *Man:* Switzerland
Woman: Russia and Australia
3 kangaroos, mountain scenery, Moscow, surfing beaches, Red Square, a ski resort

Lesson 33

SOUNDS
3 /eɪ/: age face pay plate stay take
/æ/: back bag crash exam
/ɑː/: park car sharp

GRAMMAR AND VOCABULARY
1 stolen fallen left come kept broken run caught hurt paid lost found
2 1 has stolen 2 has caught 3 have lost 4 has fallen 5 have found 6 have broken
3 a ✓ have never visited b ✗ visited c ✓ have read d ✓ have just had

e ✓ Have you done ... yet
f ✓ has hurt g ✗ did you go
h ✗ visited, had

4 1 went 2 have lost 3 has ever visited 4 did you come back
5 Have you taken 6 went, took
7 have just booked

READING AND LISTENING

1 1 d 2 b 3 a 4 c

3 *Suggested answers*
1 Pete has had an awful day.
2 Jan has been at the office all day.
3 Pete is tired because he has done the housework.
4 Jan has just arrived home from work.
5 Pete hasn't had time to take the car to the garage or to do the shopping.
6 Pete hasn't made the evening meal.

Lesson 34

VOCABULARY

1 *Across:* 2 matches 4 knife 6 ice
7 rubbish 9 glass
Down: 1 blanket 3 rain 5 fork
8 bag

2 1 Be careful! 2 Slow down!
3 Please sit down. 4 Excuse me.
5 Don't worry! 6 Be quiet!

GRAMMAR

1 1 c 2 e 3 a 4 f 5 d 6 b

LISTENING

1 1 Kenya 2 the airport
3 the supermarket 4 the station

2 1 They're going to Kenya to see the wildlife.
2 She's going to the airport to meet her sister.
3 He's going to the supermarket to buy some food.
4 She's going to the station to get the tickets.

READING AND WRITING

1 no

3 1 E 2 B 3 D 4 A 5 C

Lesson 35

VOCABULARY AND GRAMMAR

1 good – bad quiet – noisy
careful – careless polite – rude
fast – slow early – late

2 good – well bad – badly
happy – happily fast – fast
easy – easily early – early
angry – angrily late – late
careless – carelessly
fluent – fluently clear – clearly
patient – patiently

3 1 fluently 2 good, bad
3 patiently/clearly 4 happy
5 easy, clearly 6 late/early

LISTENING

1 swimming, dancing, cooking, driving, singing

2 1 well, fast 2 good 3 badly
4 fast, slowly 5 dangerous

READING

1 southern Italy

2 quickly purposefully
passionately seriously
slowly carefully noisily

3 *Suggested answers*
They walk quickly and purposefully.
They take life seriously.
They have meetings.
They do business.
They talk on car phones.
They drive slowly.
They park carefully.

4 *Suggested answers*
They drink espressos and eat mountains of pasta.
They argue passionately.
They hang washing in the streets. They shout noisily.
They honk the horns of their scooters.

Lesson 36

VOCABULARY AND READING

1 passport control first class
check-in departure lounge
petrol station baggage reclaim
ticket office arrival hall
boarding pass

2 c h e i f a g d b

3 *Train:* 2 3 8 *Plane:* 1 4
Car: 5 7 9 *Boat:* 6 10

4 *Positive:* 3 6 8
Negative: 1 2 4 10

SOUNDS

1 a 2 a 3 b 4 a 5 b

GRAMMAR AND LISTENING

1 1 When will he go sightseeing?
2 Will you have a single room?
3 How long will you stay in London?
4 How will you get from the airport/hotel to the hotel/airport?
5 Where will you have dinner this evening.

2 1 d 2 e 3 a 4 b 5 c

4 b

5 1 She'll get up very early.
2 She'll have a big breakfast.
3 She'll visit the Louvre in the morning.
4 She'll have lunch on a boat on the River Seine.
5 She'll go up the Eiffel Tower in the afternoon.

Lesson 37

VOCABULARY

1 sunny cloudy rainy foggy
cold hot windy warm
snowy wet

2 1 D 2 C 3 F 4 A 5 B 6 E

3 *Suggested answers*
a picnic: sunshine, warm, not too hot
sailing: sunny and windy, warm
seaside holiday: sunny and hot
growing tomatoes: rain and sun
working indoors: rain, cold

SOUNDS

1 11° -1° 16° 35° -4° 24° -10°

GRAMMAR

1 1 There will be sunshine. It will be cold and very windy.
2 It will be sunny and warm. It will be a nice day.
3 There will be snow. It will be very cold.
4 It will be rainy and warm.

2 *Suggested answers*
1 It won't rain. It won't be hot.
2 It won't be cold.
3 There won't be any sunshine. It won't be a nice day.
4 It won't be sunny but it won't be cold.

4 *Suggested answers*
1 will get 2 will disappear
3 will become 4 will grow
5 will increase 6 will melt

READING AND LISTENING

1 *Suggested answers*
Pessimistic: 1 3 6 7 8 10
Optimistic: 2 4 5 9

2 The man is optimistic, the woman is pessimistic.

3 *Woman:* 1 3 *Man:* 2 9

Lesson 38

SOUNDS

1 2 No, it wasn't. It was invented by Bell.
3 No, it wasn't. It was painted by Picasso.
4 No, it wasn't. It was written by Shakespeare.
5 No, they aren't. They are made in Japan.
6 No, they weren't. They were built by the Pharaohs.

2 pottery computer tobacco
coffee compose invent
discover Japanese consume
appreciate introduce

VOCABULARY AND GRAMMAR

2 1 grow 2 built 3 discovered
4 grow 5 discovered 6 invented

3 *Present:* 1, 4 *Past:* 2, 3, 5, 6

4 2 The Blue Mosque in Istanbul was built by Sultan Ahmed.
3 Penicillin was discovered by Fleming in 1928.
4 Oranges are grown in the region of Valencia in Spain.
5 Australia was discovered by the Europeans in the 17th century.
6 Gunpowder was invented by the Chinese in the 9th century.

READING AND WRITING

1 drunk introduced appreciated
grown sold dried enjoyed
consumed heated

2 is grown are dried and heated
was first grown was introduced
is grown is sold

3 B: coffee C: tobacco

Lesson 39

GRAMMAR

1 1 'It's open all year.'
2 'It starts at half past nine.'
3 'Dinner is served at seven.'
4 'We're late because of the traffic.'
5 'I don't like the food.'
6 'I'm not staying another night.'

2 1 was 2 leaves 3 cost 4 were
5 was 6 is 7 was 8 finished

3 1 He said it wasn't far from the town centre.
2 She said she didn't like opera.
3 She said the bus arrived at 9 o'clock.
4 The manager said that they had a double room.
5 He said it cost thirty pounds a night.
6 She said the train took half an hour.
7 They said they didn't want a television in the room.
8 He said they were early and that it didn't leave until six thirty.

LISTENING AND READING

1 1 c 2 d 3 b 4 a

3 and 4 8.00 (8.30); cheaper (easier); 7.00 (7.15); in the office all day (out all day)

5 Maria phoned... She said she could meet you for coffee...
She said that if you didn't phone back... She also said she had got the books... And they only cost £5 each

Lesson 40

READING

1 1 Maria. 2 She is writing to Anna.
3 She is in Hastings in Britain.
4 She is on an English course.

2 1 d 2 b 3 c 4 a

3 *Suggested answers*
Present simple: As you know, we work, we go, the course finishes, I don't know
Present continuous: I'm enjoying, I'm staying
Present perfect: I haven't written, I have been busy, I've met, I've seen
Past simple: I left home, I travelled, the ferry journey wasn't nice, I saw
Future: I won't travel, what I'll do, I'll stay, It'll be, My English will be

GRAMMAR

1 1 went: past simple
2 'm staying: present continuous
3 'll come: future
4 haven't met: present perfect
5 like: present simple

2 1 b 2 e 3 a 4 c 5 d

3 won bought said stepped
sold sent told got made
arrived left lost read
climbed hurt found

4 1 met 2 has just come back
3 have lost 4 won 5 Have you read 6 arrived 7 haven't done
8 did they leave

5 1 am staying 2 takes
3 don't like 4 is not playing
5 work 6 Do you often go

6 1 3 6

Wordlist

The first number after each word shows the lesson in which the word first appears in the vocabulary box. The numbers in *italics* show the later lessons in which the word appears again.

address /əˈdres/ 3
adult /ædʌlt/ 39
afternoon /ˌɑːftəˈnuːn/ 7
age /eɪdʒ/ 3
airport /ˈeəpɔːt/ 12
album /ˈælbəm/ 16-20
appear /əˈpɪə(r)/ 18
apple /ˈæp(ə)l/ 17
apple pie /ˈæpe(ə)l paɪ/ 25
April /ˈeɪprɪl/ 22
arm /ɑːm/ 28, *33*
armchair /ɑːmˈtʃeə(r)/ 8
arrival hall /əˈraɪv(ə)l hɔːl/ 36
artist /ˈɑːtɪst/ 2
aspirin /ˈæsprɪn/ 28
at the back /æt ðə bæk/ 8
at the front /æt ðə frʌnt/ 8
attractive /əˈtræktɪv/ 15, *16-20, 19*
August /ˈɔːgəst/ 22
aunt /ɑˈnt/ 6
Australia /ɒːstreɪlɪə/ 1
Austria /ˈɒstrɪə/ 20

back /bæk/ 28
bacon /ˈbeɪkən/ 17
badly /ˈbædlɪ/ 35
bad–tempered /bæd ˈtempəd/ 16
bag /bæg/ 5, *33*
baggage reclaim /ˈbægɪdʒ rɪˈkleɪm/ 36
baker /ˈbeɪkə(r)/ 14
ballet /ˈbæleɪ/ 11-15
banana /bəˈnɑːnə/ 17
Bangkok /ˈbæŋkɒk/ 1
bank /bæŋk/ 14
bar /bɑː(r)/ 26
barbecue /ˈbɑːbɪˌkjuː/ 34
basketball /ˈbɑːskɪtˌbɔːl/ 30
bath /bɑːθ/ 8
bathroom /ˈbɑːθruːm/ 8
beard /ˈbɪəd/ 19
beautiful /ˈbjuːtɪˌfʊl/ 4, *15*
bed /bed/ 8
bedroom /ˈbedruːm/ 8
beef /biːf/ 17
beer /bɪə(r)/ 25
bicycle /ˈbaɪsɪk(ə)l/ 12
big /bɪg/ 15, *29*
bill /bɪl/ 33
biscuits /ˈbɪskɪtz/ 26
black /blæk/ 5
blanket /ˈblæŋkɪt/ 34
blue /bluː/ 5
boarding pass /bɔːdɪŋ pɑːs/ 36
boat /bəʊt/ 34
book /bʊk/ 4, *5*
bookcase /ˈbʊkkeɪs/ 8
bookshop /ˈbʊkʃɒp/ 14
boring /ˈbɔːrɪŋ/ 15
bottle /ˈbɒt(ə)l/ 26
bottle opener /ˈbɒt(ə)l ˈəʊpənə(r)/ 34
box /bɒks/ 26
boxing /bɒksɪŋ/ 26-30
boyfriend /ˈbɔɪfrend/ 6, *40*
Brazil /brəˈzɪl/ 1
bread /bred/ 16-20, *17*
break /breɪk/ 33
breakfast /ˈbrekfəst/ 7
bridge /brɪdʒ/ 32
Britain /brɪt(ə)n/ 1
brother /ˈbrʌðə(r)/ 6
brown /braʊn/ 5
Budapest /buːdəpest/ 1, *20*
bunch /bʌntʃ/ 26
bus /bʌs/ 12
bus stop /bʌs stɒp/ 12
business class /ˈbɪznɪs klɒːs/ 36
butter /ˈbʌtə(r)/ 16-20, *17*
buy /baɪ/ 20

café /ˈkæfeɪ/ 4, *11-15*
cakes /keɪkz/ 26
calculator /ˈkælkjʊˌleɪtə(r)/ 5
camera /ˈkæmrə/ 5
camping /kæmpɪŋ/ 39
camp site /kæmp saɪt/ 28
Canada /ˈkænədə/ 1
car /kɑː(r)/ 12, *33*
car park /kɑː(r) pɑːk/ 4, *14, 39*
caravan /ˈkærəˌvæn/ 26-30
carefully /ˈkeəfʊlɪ/ 35
carelessly /ˈkeələslɪ/ 35
carrot /ˈkærət/ 17
carton /ˈkɑːt(ə)n/ 34
cassette /kæˈset/ 4
casual /ˈkæʒʊəl/ 23
catch /kætʃ/ 33
cathedral /kəˈθiːdr(ə)l/ 32
centigrade /ˈsentɪˌgreɪd/ 29
centimetre /ˈsentɪˌmiːtə(r)/ 29
chair /tʃeə(r)/ 4, *8*
change /tʃeɪndʒ/ 24
charges /tʃɑːdʒas/ 39
cheap /tʃiːp/ 12
cheap day return /tʃiːp daɪ rɪˈtɜːn/ 36
check-in /ˈtʃek ɪn/ 38
cheerful /ˈtʃɪəfʊl/ 16-20
cheese /tʃiːz/ 17
cheesecake /ˈtʃiːzkeɪk/ 25
chemist /ˈkemɪst/ 14
chicken /ˈtʃɪkɪn/ 17
Chinese food /tʃarˈniːz fuːd/ 10
chocolate mousse /ˈtʃɒkələt muːs/ 25
chocolates /ˈtʃɒkələtz/ 26
cinema /ˈsɪnɪˌmɑː/ 14
classical music /ˈklæsɪk(ə)l ˈmjuːzɪk/ 10
classroom /ˈklɑːsruːm/ 4
climb /klaɪm/ 32
climbing /klaɪmɪŋ/ 30
cloud /klaʊd/ 37
coach /kəʊtʃ/ 12
coat /kəʊt/ 5
Coca-cola /ˌkəʊkəˌkəʊlə/ 25
coffee /ˈkɒfɪ/ 17
coffee bar /ˈkɒfɪ bɑː(r)/ 40
cold /kəʊld/ 29, *37*
cold (*noun*) /kəʊld/ 28
comb /kəʊm/ 5
comfortable /ˈkʌmftəb(ə)l/ 23
computer /kəmˈpjuːtə(r)/ 4
concerto /kənˈtʃeətəʊ/ 11-15
cook /kʊk/ 13
cook dinner /kʊk ˈdɪnə(r)/ 11
cooker /ˈkʊkə(r)/ 8
cooking /ˈkʊkɪŋ/ 10
cool /kuːl/ 37
cough /kɒf/ 28
cough medicine /kɒf ˈmedsɪn/ 28
cover /ˈkʌvə(r)/ 31
crash /kræʃ/ 33
crowded /kraʊdɪd/ 12
cup /kʌp/ 34
cupboard /ˈkʌbəd/ 8
curly /ˈkɜːlɪ/ 19
curtains /ˈkɜːt(ə)nz/ 8
cut /kʌt/ 33
cycling /ˈsaɪklɪŋ/ 30

dancing /dɑːnsɪŋ/ 10
dangerous /ˈdeɪndʒərəs/ 30
dark /dɑːk/ 19
daughter /ˈdɔːtə(r)/ 6
December /dɪˈsembə(r)/ 22
decide /dɪˈsaɪd/ 18
departure gate /dɪˈpɑːtʃə(r) geɪt/ 36
departure lounge /dɪˈpɑːtʃə(r) laʊndʒ/ 36
detective story /dɪˈtektɪv ˈstɔːrɪ/ 21
diary /ˈdaɪərɪ/ 5
difficult /ˈdɪfɪkəlt/ 30
dining room /daɪnɪŋ ruːm/ 8
dinner /ˈdɪnə(r)/ 7
director /daɪˈrektə(r)/ 40
discover /dɪskʌvə(r)/ 38
disappear /ˌdɪsəˈpɪə(r)/ 21
dishwasher /ˈdɪʃwɒʃə(r)/ 8
divorced /dɪˈvɔːsd/ 16-20, *21*
dizzy /ˈdɪzɪ/ 28
do /duː/ 13, *20*
do some work/homework /duː sʌm wɜːk/həʊmwɜːk/ 11
do the housework /duː ðə ˈhaʊswɜːk/ 11
do the washing up /duː ðə ˈwɒʃɪŋ ʌp/ 11
doctor /ˈdɒktə(r)/ 2
double room /ˈdʌb(ə)l ruːm/ 28
downstairs /daʊnˈsteəz/ 8
draw /drɔˈ/ 13
dress /dres/ 23
drink coffee /drɪŋk ˈkɒfɪ/ 9
drive /draɪv/ 12
drop /drɒp/ 33
dry /draɪ/ 29, *37*
eat an apple /iːt æn ˈæp(ə)l/ 9

egg /eg/ 17
eight /eɪt/ 4
eighteen /erˈtːn/ 4
eighth /eɪtθ/ 22
eighty /ˈeɪtɪ/ 4
elderly /ˈeldəlɪ/ 19
eleven /ɪˈlev(ə)n/ 4
eleventh /ɪˈlevənθ/ 22
engineer /ˌendʒɪˈnɪə(r)/ 2
England /ˈɪnglənd/ 20
evening /ˈiːvnɪŋ/ 7
exam /ɪgˈzæm/ 33
exciting /ɪkˈsaɪtɪŋ/ 30
Excuse me /ɪkˈskjuːz miː/ 11-15
expensive /ɪkˈspensɪv/ 12, *30*
eyes /aɪz/ 19

facilities /fæsɪlɪtɪs/ 39
fail /feɪl/ 33
faint /feɪnt/ 28
fair /feə(r)/ 19
far /fɑː(r)/ 12
farmer /ˈfɑːmə(r)/ 2
fashionable/ˈfæʃnəb(ə)l/ 23,*30*
fast /fɑːst/ 12, *29*

father /ˈfɑːðə(r)/ 6
February /ˈfebrʊərɪ/ 22
ferry /ˈferɪ/ 12
fifteen /fɪfˈtiːn/ 4
fifth /fɪfθ/ 22
fifty /ˈfɪftɪ/ 4
find /faɪnd/ 20, *21, 28, 33*
finger /ˈfɪŋgə(r)/ 30, *35*
finish /ˈfɪnɪʃ/ 7
fire /ˈfaɪə(r)/ 8
first /fɜːst/ 22
first class /fɜːst klɑːs/ 38
first name /fɜːst neɪm/ 3
five /faɪv/ 4
florist /ˈflɒrɪst/ 14
flowers /ˈflaʊə(r)z/ 26
fly /flaɪ/ 20
fog /fɒg/ 37
foggy /ˈfɒgɪ/ 37
foot /fʊt/ 28
football /ˈfʊtbɔːl/ 10, *30*
foreigner /ˈfɒrɪnə(r)/ 40
forget /fəˈget/ 40
fork /fɔːk/ 34
forty /ˈfɔːtɪ/ 4
four /fɔː(r)/ 4
fourteen /fɔːˈtiːn/ 4
fourth /fɔːθ/ 22
France /frɑːns/ 20
French fries /frentʃ fraɪz/ 25
fridge /frɪdʒ/ 8
friendly /ˈfrendlɪ/ 4, *16-20*
fruit /fruːt/ 26

garage /ˈgærɑːdʒ/ 8
garden /ˈgɑːd(ə)n/ 8
get /get/ 12, *24*
get the bus/train to work/ school/home /get ðə bʌs/treɪn tə wɜːk/skuːl/həʊm/ 11
get up /get ʌp/ 7
girlfriend /ˈgɜːlfrend/ 6
glass /glɑːs/ 27
glasses /glɑːsɪz/ 5, *19*
go /gəʊ/ 20
go by /gəʊ baɪ/ 12
go running /gəʊ ˈrʌnɪŋ/ 9
go shopping /gəʊ ˈʃɒpɪŋ/ 11
go to bed /gəʊ tə bed/ 7
go to the cinema /gəʊ tə ðə ˈsɪnɪˌmɑː/ 11
go to work/school /gəʊ tə wɜːk/skuːl/ 7
goal /gəʊl/ 33
going to parties /ˈgəʊɪŋ tə ˈpɑːtɪz/ 10
going to the cinema /ˈgəʊɪŋ tə ðə ˈsɪnɪˌmɑː/ 10
going to the theatre /ˈgəʊɪŋ tə ðə ˈθɪətə(r)/ 10
golf /gɒlf/ 32
good /gʊd/ 4
good-looking /gʊd ˈlʊkɪŋ/ 19, *16-20*
grandfather /ˈgrænˌfɑːðə(r)/ 6
grandmother /ˈgrænˌmʌðə(r)/ 6
grapes /greɪpz/ 17
green /griːn/ 5
greengrocer /ˈgriˈnˌgrəʊsə(r)/ 14
grey /greɪ/ 5
grow /grəʊ/ 38
guest /gest/ 21

hair /heə(r)/ 19
hamburger /ˈhæmˌbɜːgə(r)/ 25
hand /hænd/ 28
hang gliding /ˈhæŋˌglaɪdɪŋ/ 30
happy /ˈhæpɪ/ 16
have /hæv/ 20
have a shower /hæv eɪ ˈʃaʊə(r)/ 9
headache /ˈhedeɪk/ 28
heavy /ˈhevɪ/ 27
high /haɪ/ 29
hit record /hɪt ˈrekɔːd/ 16-20
home /həʊm/ 21
horseriding /ˈhɔːsraɪdɪŋ/ 30
hot /hɒt/ 29, *37*
hotel /həʊˈtel/ 21, *28*
Hungary /ˈhʌŋgə(r)ɪ/ 1, *20*
husband /ˈhʌzbənd/ 6, *21*

ice /aɪs/ 34
ice cream /aɪs kriːm/ 25
ill /ɪl/ 28
in the garden /ɪn ðə ˈgɑːd(ə)n/ 8
in the mountains /ɪn ðə ˈmaʊntɪns/ 15
indoors /ɪnˈdɔːz/ 8
industrial /ɪnˈdʌstrɪəl/ 15
interesting /ˈɪntrəstɪŋ/ 4, *15*
international /ˌɪntəˈnæʃən(ə)l/ 4
invent /ɪnvent/ 38
invite /ɪnˈvaɪt/ 24
Italy /ˈɪtəlɪ/ 20

jacket /ˈdʒækɪt/ 23
January /ˈdʒænjʊərɪ/ 22
Japan /dʒəˈpæn/ 1
jazz /dʒæz/ 10
jeans /dʒiːnz/ 23, *26*
job /dʒɒb/ 3
judo /ˈdʒuˈdəʊ/ 11-15
juice /dʒuːs/ 17
July /dʒuːˈlaɪ/ 22
June /dʒuːn/ 22

kebab /kɪˈbæb/ 25
keys /kiːz/ 5
kill /kɪl/ 21
kilometre /ˈkɪləˌmiːtə(r)/ 29
kilometres per hour /ˈkɪləˌmiːtə(r)z pɜː(r) aʊə(r)/ 29
kind /kaɪnd/ 4
kiss /kɪs/ 31
kitchen /ˈkɪtʃɪn/ 8
knife /naɪf/ 34

lamb /læm/ 17
lamp /læmp/ 8
language school /ˈlæŋgwɪdʒ skuːl/ 40
large /lɑːdʒ/ 27
laugh /lɑːf/ 23
lazy /ˈleɪzɪ/ 16
learn /lɜːn/ 18
learn the guitar /lɜːn ðə gɪtɑː(r)/ 9
leather /ˈleðə(r)/ 27
left /left/ 21
leg /leg/ 28
lemon /ˈlemən/ 17
lettuce /ˈletɪs/ 17
library /ˈlaɪbrərɪ/ 4, *14*
lift /lɪft/ 33
light /laɪt/ 27
listen /ˈlɪs(ə)n/ 20
listen to the radio /ˈlɪs(ə)n tə ðə reidɪəʊ/ 9
live /lɪv laɪv/ 18
lively /laɪvlɪ/ 15
London /ˈlʌnd(ə)n/ 1, *20*
long /lɒŋ/ 19, *27*
lose /luːz/ 20, *33*
loudly /laʊdlɪ/ 37
love /lʌv/ 40
lovely /ˈlʌvlɪ/ 15
low /ləʊ/ 29
lunch /lʌntʃ/ 7

magazines /ˌmægəˈziːnz/ 10
make friends /meɪk frendz/ 20
make /meɪk/ 38
March /mɑːtʃ/ 22
market /ˈmɑːkɪt/ 14
marriage /ˈmærɪdʒ/ 16-20, *21*
married /ˈmærɪd/ 3
marry /ˈmærɪ/ 18
matches /mætʃɪz/ 36
May /meɪ/ 22
mayonnaise /ˌmeɪəˈneɪz/ 25
meal /miːl/ 16-20

medium-height /ˈmiːdɪəm haɪt/ 19
metal /ˈmet(ə)l/ 27
metre /ˈmiːtə(r)/ 29
Mexico /ˈmeksɪkaʊ/ 1
midday /ˈmɪddeɪ/ 7
middle–aged /ˈmɪd(ə)l eɪdʒd/ 19
millimetre /ˈmɪlɪˌmiːtə(r)/ 29
miss /mɪs/ 33, *40*
mobile phone /ˈməʊbaɪl fəʊn/ 5
modern /ˈmɒd(ə)n/ 15
morning /ˈmɔːnɪŋ/ 7
mother /ˈmʌðə(r)/ 6
motor racing /ˈməʊtə(r) reɪsɪŋ/ 30
motorbike /ˈməʊtə(r) baɪk/ 12
moustache /məˈstɑːʃ/ 19
mystery /ˈmɪstərɪ/ 21

naughty /ˈnɔːtɪ/ 16
near /nɪə(r)/ 12
newsagent /ˈnjuːzˌeɪdʒ(ə)nt/ 14
night /naɪt/ 7
nine /naɪn/ 4
nineteen /naɪntiːn/ 4
ninety one /ˈnaɪntɪ wʌn/ 4
ninth /naɪnθ/ 22
north east /nɔːθ iːst/ 15
north west /nɔːθ west/ 15
notebook /ˈnəʊtbʊk/ 5
November /nəˈvembə(r)/ 22
nylon /ˈnaɪlɒn/ 27

October /ɒkˈtəʊbə(r)/ 22
oil /ɔɪl/ 17
old /əʊld/ 15, *19, 29*
on an island /ɒn æn ˈaɪlənd/ 15
on the coast /ɒn ðə kəʊst/ 15
on the river /ɒn ðə ˈrɪvə(r)/ 15
one hundred /wʌn ˈhʌndrəd/ 4
onion /ˈʌnjən/ 17
orange /ˈɒrɪndʒ/ 17
outdoors /aʊtˈdɔːz/ 8

packet /ˈpækɪt/ 26
paint /peint/ 38
pair /peə(r)/ 26
paper /ˈpeɪpə(r)/ 27
Pardon /ˈpɑːd(ə)n/ 11-15
Paris /ˈpærɪs/ 20
park /pɑːk/ 32
pass /pɑːs/ 33
passport control /ˈpɑːspɔːt kənˈtrəʊl/ 36
pasta /ˈpæstə/ 25
pay /peɪ/ 33
peach /piːʃ/ 17

pen /pen/ 5
pencil /ˈpensɪl/ 5
perfume /ˈpɜːfjuːm/ 26
personal stereo
/ˈpɜːsən(ə)l ˈsterɪəʊ/ 5
phone box /fəʊn bɒks/ 14
phone number
/fəʊn ˈnʌmbə(r)/ 3
pink /pɪŋk/ 5
pizza /ˈpiːtsə/ 25
plane /pleɪn/ 12, *36*
plastic /ˈplæstɪk/ 27
plate /pleɪt/ 33
platform /ˈplætfɔːm/ 36
play /pleɪ/ 13, *18*
play football /pleɪ ˈfʊtbɔːl/ 9
player /ˈpleɪə(r)/ 4
Please /pliːz/ 11-15
point at /pɔɪnt æt/ 31
police officer
/pəˈliːs ˈɒfɪsə(r)/ 2
polite /pəˈlaɪt/ 16-20
politely /pəˈlaɪtlɪ/ 35
popular /ˈpɒpjʊlə(r)/ 4, *30*
post office /pəʊst ˈɒfɪs/ 14
potato /pəˈteɪtəʊ/ 17
pretty /ˈprɪtɪ/ 19
pub /pʌb/ 14
purple /ˈpɜːp(ə)l/ 5

quickly /kwɪklɪ/ 35
quietly /ˈkwaɪətlɪ/ 35

railway station
/ˈreɪlweɪ ˈsteɪʃ(ə)n/ 14
rain /reɪn/ 37
rainy /reɪnɪ/ 37
read /riːd/ 20
read a newspaper
/riːd ə ˈnjuːsˌpeɪpə(r)/ 9
receive /rɪˈsiːv/ 18
reception desk
/rɪˈsepʃ(ə)n desk/ 4
receptionist /rɪˈsepʃənɪst/ 2
rectangular
/rekˈtæŋgʊlə(r)/ 27
red /red/ 5
restaurant /ˈrestəˌrɒnt/ 14, *16-20*
return /rɪˈtɜːn/ 36
rice /raɪs/ 17
ride /raɪd/ 12, *13*
ring /rɪŋ/ 5
risotto /rɪˈzɒtəʊ/ 25
rock music /rɒk ˈmjuːzɪk/ 10
room service /ruːm ˈsɜːvɪs/ 28
round /raʊnd/ 27
rubbish /ˈrʌbɪʃ/ 34
rudely /ruːdlɪ/ 35
salad /ˈsæləd/ 25

samba /ˈsæmbə/ 11-15
sandwich /ˈsænwɪdʒ/ 25
sauna /ˈsɔːnə/ 11-15
save /seɪv/ 24
score /skɔː(r)/ 33
sea /siː/ 40
second /ˈsekənd/ 22
secretary /ˈsekrɪətrɪ/ 2
see friends /siː frendz/ 11
self–study room /self ˈstʌdɪ ruːm/ 4
September /sepˈtembə(r)/ 22
serious /ˈsɪərɪəs/ 16
seven /ˈsev(ə)n/ 4
seventeen /ˌsevənˈtiːn/ 4
seventh /ˈsev(ə)nθ/ 22
seventy /ˈsevəntɪ/ 4
shake hands /ʃeɪk hændz/ 31
shirt /ʃɜːt/ 23
shoes /ʃuːz/ 23
short /ʃɔːt/ 19, *27*
shorts /ʃɔːtz/ 23
shower /ˈʃʊə(r)/ 8
shy /ʃaɪ/ 16
sick /sɪk/ 30
siesta /sɪˈestə/ 11-15
single /ˈsɪŋg(ə)l/ 36
single room
/ˈsɪŋg(ə)l ruːm/ 28
sister /ˈsɪstə(r)/ 6
sit down /sɪt daʊn/ 23
sitting room /sɪtɪŋ ruːm/ 8
six /sɪks/ 4
sixteen /ˌsɪksˈtiːn/ 4
sixth /sɪksθ/ 22
sixty /ˈsɪkstɪ/ 4
ski /skiː/ 13
skiing /skiːɪŋ/ 30
skirt /skɜːt/ 23
slim /slɪm/ 19
slow /sləʊ/ 12, *29*
slowly /sləʊlɪ/ 35
small /smɔːl/ 15, *19, 27, 29*
smart /smɑːt/ 23
smile /smaɪl/ 23
snow /snəʊ/ 37
soap /səʊp/ 26
socks /sɒks/ 23
sofa /ˈsəʊfə/ 8
son /sʌn/ 6
sore throat /sɔː(r) θrəʊt/ 28
Sorry /ˈsɒrɪ/ 11-15
south east /saʊθ iːst/ 15
south west /saʊθ west/ 15
spaghetti /spəˈgetɪ/ 11-15
speak /spiːk/ 13
spend /spend/ 24
square /skweə(r)/ 27, *29*
stand /stænd/ 23
start /stɑːt/ 7, *18*

station /ˈsteɪʃ(ə)n/ 12, *14*
stay /steɪ/ 20
steak /steɪk/ 25
steal /stiːl/ 33
step /step/ 40
stomach ache
/ˈstʌmək eɪk/ 28
straight /streɪt/ 19
strange /streɪndʒ/ 40
strawberry /ˈstrɔːbərɪ/ 25
stubborn /ˈstʌbən/ 16
student /ˈstjuːd(ə)nt/ 2
study /ˈstʌdɪ/ 8
successful /səkˈsesfʊl/ 21
suit /suːt/ 23
sun /sʌn/ 37
sunny /sʌnɪ/ 37
supermarket /ˈsuːpəˌmɑːkɪt/ 14
surname /ˈsɜːneɪm/ 3
sweater /ˈswetə(r)/ 23
swim /swɪm/ 13
swimming /swɪmɪŋ/ 10, *30*
swimsuit /ˈswɪmsuːt/ 23
Switzerland /swɪtsəlænd/ 20

table /ˈteɪb(ə)l/ 4, *8*
take /teɪk/ 12, *20, 24*
take off /teɪk ɒf/ 31
tall /tɔːl/ 19
taxi driver /ˈtæksɪ ˈdraɪvə(r)/ 2
taxi rank /ˈtæksɪ ræŋk/ 14
tea /tiː/ 17
teacher /ˈtiːtʃə(r)/ 2
television /ˈtelɪˌvɪʒ(ə)n/ 8
tell /tel/ 21
temperature /ˈtemprɪtʃə(r)/ 28
tennis /ˈtenɪs/ 10, *30*
tent /tent/ 28
tenth /tenθ/ 22
Thailand / taɪlænd/ 1
Thank you /θæŋk juː/ 11-15
third /θɜːd/ 22
thirteen /θɜːˈtiːn/ 4
thirty /ˈθɜːtɪ/ 4
three /θriː/ 4
ticket office /ˈtɪkɪt ˈɒfɪs/ 36
tie /taɪ/ 23
tights /taɪts/ 23
tired /ˈtaɪəd/ 28
tiring /ˈtaɪərɪŋ/ 30
toe /təʊ/ 28
toilet /ˈtɔɪlɪt/ 8
Tokyo /ˈtaʊkɪəʊ/ 1
tomato /təˈmɑːtəʊ/ 17
tourist class /ˈtʊərɪst klɑːs/ 36
train /treɪn/ 12, *33, 36*
trainers /ˈtreɪnə(r)s/ 23
tram /træm/ 12
travel /træv(ə)l/ 39
trousers /ˈtraʊzəz/ 23

twelth /twelfθ/ 22
type /taɪp/ 13
T–shirt /tiː ʃɜːt/ 23

ugly /ˈʌglɪ/ 15
uncle /ˈʌŋk(ə)l/ 6
underground
/ˌʌndəˈgraʊnd/ 12
unhappy /ʌnˈhæpɪ/ 21
upstairs /ʌpˈsteəz/ 8
use /juːz/ 13

Venice /ˈvenɪs/ 20
vet /vet/ 2
Vienna /vɪənə/ 20
view /vjuː/ 34
visit /ˈvɪzɪt/ 20

waiter /ˈweɪtə(r)/ 2, *21*
wake–up call
/weɪk ʌp kɔːl/ 28
wallet /ˈwɒlɪt/ 5, *33*
warm /wɔːm/ 23, *37*
washbasin /wɒʃ ˈbeɪs(ə)n/ 8
watch /wɒtʃ/ 5, *20*
watch a tennis match
/wɒtʃ ə tenɪs mætʃ/ 9
watching sport
/wɒtʃɪŋ spɔːt/ 10
water /ˈwɔːtə(r)/ 17
wear /weə(r)/ 23
weekend /wiːkˈend/ 7
well /wel/ 35
well–behaved
/wel bɪˈheɪvd/ 16-20
well–built /wel bɪlt/ 19
wet /wet/ *29, 37*
white /waɪt/ 5
wife /waɪf/ 6
wind /wɪnd/ 37
windsurfing /ˈwɪndˌsɜːfɪŋ/ 30
windy /wɪndɪ/ 37
wine /waɪn/ 17, *25, 26*
wood /wʊd/ 27
work /wɜːk/ 7, *18*
write /raɪt/ 13, *20, 38*
writer /ˈraɪtə(r)/ 21

yellow /ˈjeləʊ/ 5
young /jʌŋ/ 19, *29*
youth hostel /juːθ ˈhɒst(ə)l/ 39

Zurich /ˈzjuːrɪk/ 20

Wordbank

Use the categories below to help you organise new vocabulary. Try and write each new word in at least two different categories. You may also like to write down words which often go with the new vocabulary items

character	clothes	countries and nationalities
crime and justice	customs and traditions	daily life
days, months, seasons	education	environmental issues
family and friends	food and drink	geographical features and locations
health and physical feelings	house and home	language learning
leisure interests	the media	parts of the body
personal information	personal possessions	physical appearance
politics, government and society	religion	shops and shopping
social situations	town features and facilities	transport
travel	work	weather

Macmillan Education
Between Towns Road
Oxford OX4 3PP
A division of Macmillan Publishers Limited
Companies and representatives throughout the world

ISBN-13 : 978 0 435 24209 1

First published 1997.

Designed by Giles Davies

Cover design by Stafford & Stafford

Illustrations by
Phil Bannister, pp12, 13, 38, 46
Kathy Baxendale, pp28, 49, 74
Jerry Collins, pp26, 46, 54, 68
Frances Lloyd, pp7, 53, 56, 63
Judy Stevens, pp10, 27
Darrel Warner, pp3, 4, 48
Gary Wing, p11

Acknowledgements

The authors and publishers would like to thank the following for their kind permission to reproduce material in this book:

David Higham Associates on behalf of Keith Waterhouse for an adapted extract from *The Theory and Practice of Travel* published by Coronet Books; Reed Consumer Books Ltd. for an adapted extract from *Neither Here Nor There* by Bill Bryson published by Martin Secker & Warburg Ltd.

Photographs by: Image Bank: p44(l); Kobal Collection: pp37(tl,bc); Sarah Meadows: p20; Rex Features: p37(tr); Tony Stone: pp14, 24(c), 31(a,c), 41, 44(r), 60; Zefa: pp24(a,b), 31(b), 35,

While every effort has been made to trace the owners of copyright material in this book, there have been some cases when the publishers have been unable to contact the owners. We should be grateful to hear from anyone who recognises their copyright material and who is unacknowledged. We shall be pleased to make the necessary amendments in future editions of the book.

Printed and bound in Thailand

2009 2008 2007

24 23 22 21 20 19